100

LARGE PRINT CROSSWORD PUZZLES

(PUZZLE BOOK FOR ADULTS)

GAME NEST

Get All Our
New Releases
For Free!

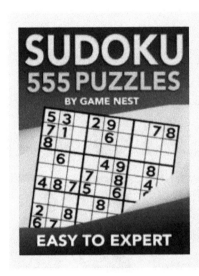

Sign up to our
VIP Newsletter
to get all of our future releases
absolutely free!

www.gamenest.org/free

CROSSWORD
PUZZLES

CROSSWORD 01

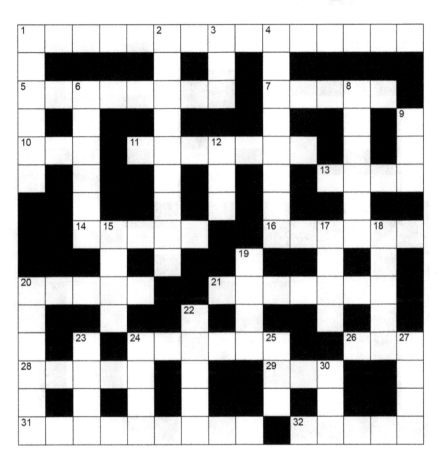

Across

1 Herb Gardner play (15)
5 Removed from the actual action, as with a commentator (8)
7 Prestidigitator's props (5)
10 He replaced Foxx as baseball's youngest player when he debuted at age 17 in 1926 (3)
11 Boston's county (7)
13 1700, on cornerstones (4)
14 Cranial cavity (5)
16 With logic (6)
20 __ Day (tree-planting celebration) (5)
21 Craftsman offering (7)
24 Peter of CNN (6)
26 Monarch, to Monet (3)
28 After, to Antoine (5)
29 N.J. summer hrs. (3)
31 Attempt (9)
32 Hirsch of "Lone Survivor" (5)

Down

1 Like clocks with hands (6)
2 The way it is (9)
3 Realtors' org. (3)
4 Yellow flowers (8)
6 Church songs (6)
8 Defraud (6)
9 It may be heard while passing the bar (3)
12 Magical (3)
15 Aaron's golden calf, e.g. (4)
17 Smell detector (4)
18 Terminate (5)
19 It's often fenced (4)
20 Part of East Germany (6)
22 Immobile, as a gas (5)
23 "Star ___" (classic TV series featuring Klingons) (4)
24 Terrier on the silver screen (4)
25 Shatner's sci-fi drug (3)
27 German girl's name. (4)
30 Quarterback Brady (3)

CROSSWORD 02

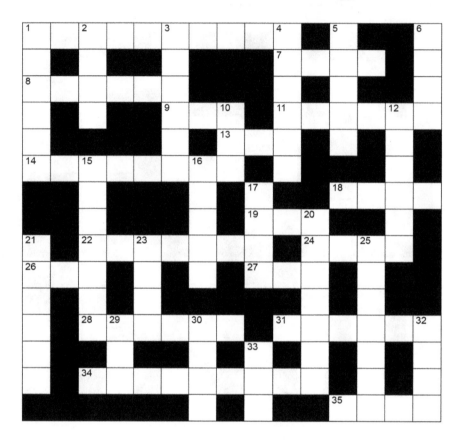

Across

1 Charm (10)
7 Father of Ahab in the Bible (4)
8 What Annabel Lee's kingdom was by (6)
9 Car owner's pmt. (3)
11 Having Coke-bottle glasses? (6)
13 Will Smith biopic (3)
14 Help in a dangerous situation (8)
18 All ___ (attentive) (4)
19 Cashless one's stop (3)
22 For example, any of the women who claimed to have had sex for money with Sen. Robert MenendeZ (7)
24 Vidi, in Caesar's boast (4)
26 Contingency ____ (3)
27 Gp. (3)
28 Smear with oil (6)
31 One of a Biblical tribe (6)
34 Like some unreliable evidence (9)
35 Laurel of slapstick (4)

Down

1 Butterfly-attracting flowers (6)
2 Stadium part (4)
3 Danes of "My So-Called Life" (6)
4 Average Joe, in Internet slang (6)
5 ___ for Sleep (5)
6 On ____ (4)
10 Oscar- and Grammy-winning singer Smith (3)
12 One right after the other (6)
15 Adam Yahiye Gadahn's group (7)
16 Lancaster County folk (5)
17 Cousin of Sven (4)
20 Archangel in Daniel (7)
21 Maker of Lipitor and Celebrex (6)
23 Letters to ___ (4)
25 Palest (7)
29 Monsieur's refusal (3)
30 Rubens subject (4)
32 McGregor of "Fargo" (4)
33 1993 New York City Marathon winner Pippig (3)

CROSSWORD 03

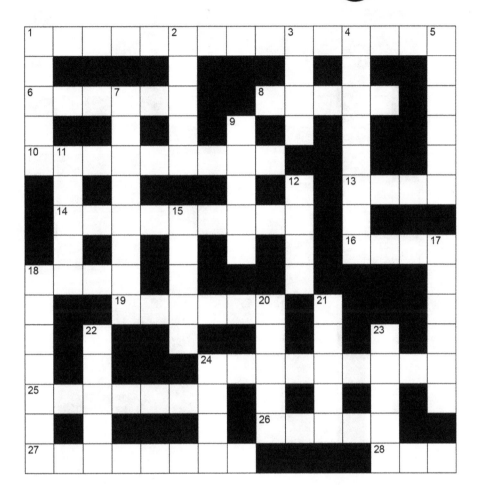

Across

1 Some insurance company employees (15)
6 How some stir-fry dishes are served (6)
8 Up the ante on eBay (5)
10 Bizarre (9)
13 Glazier's glass piece (4)
14 Most modish (9)
16 Act of 1930's (4)
18 Toward the windless side (4)
19 Retirement dinners, often (6)
24 Exhibit for an industry (9)
25 Give a scent to (7)
26 Burning coal (5)
27 All of us (8)
28 Affirmative answer (3)

Down

1 Exact match (5)
2 Semifrozen downpour (5)
3 Chemistry Nobelist Harold (4)
4 Sudden collapse into failure (8)
5 Parlor furniture (6)
7 Refreshing beverage (8)
9 More suitable (5)
11 Heavy-hitting Fielder (5)
12 Dance unit (4)
15 A violin, for short (5)
17 Arabian classic romance. (6)
18 Apple pie order? (7)
20 Weighing instrument (5)
21 Sharp of tongue (5)
22 Unisex fragrance (5)
23 "Mr. Smith Goes to Washington" director (5)
24 Ump follower (4)

CROSSWORD 04

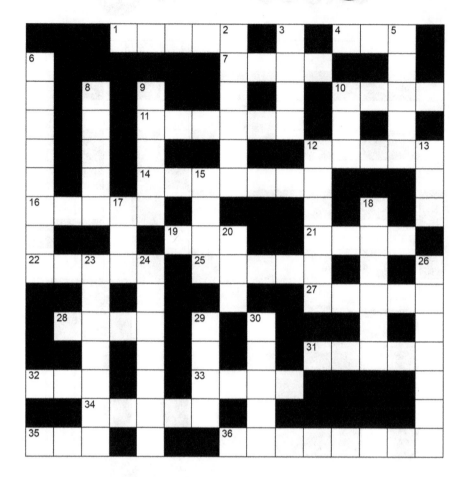

Across

1. Used a FedEx Office service (5)
4. Neat end? (3)
7. Nose to nose (4)
10. Counterfeiter-catching agt. (4)
11. Incipient forest (6)
12. Mark down, perhaps (5)
14. Painter with a museum in Santa Fe (7)
16. Peaceful protest (hyph.) (5)
19. Kobo ___, Japanese writer (3)
21. Holiday one week before the start of janvier (4)
22. Green ____ (5)
25. Suffix with form (5)
27. Reward for a pet trick (5)
28. Did handwork (4)
31. Half of a "Star Wars" character's name who has been in all six (soon to be seven!) movies (5)
32. Self-titled 2001 album (3)
33. Bump on ___ (epitome of idleness) (4)
34. Country bordering Togo (5)
35. Roadside warning (3)
36. Possessed useful information (on) (8)

Down

2. Step (6)
3. One of a pair of towel markings (4)
5. Eucalyptus-munching animal (5)
6. Like a coral reef (8)
8. Aftermath of an iron shot (5)
9. Silk substitute (5)
10. Title word. (3)
12. Calf's stomach lining (6)
13. Chew on it (3)
15. Italian island near Corsica (4)
17. Burning feeling (3)
18. Make firm (6)
20. Space invaders (3)
23. 1970 John Wayne Western (7)
24. Bear ___ (JPMorgan Chase merger partner) (7)
26. "I'll get this" (7)
29. Stylishness (4)
30. Shopper's mecca of old (5)

CROSSWORD 05

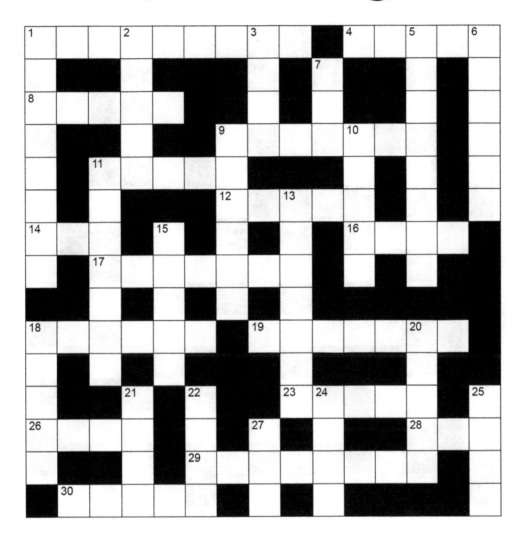

Across

1 Nylons (9)
4 Guffaws (5)
8 Love, to Dean Martin (5)
9 Ring in a crib (7)
11 "All I Need ___" Hillsong United (5)
12 Homeless person, of a sort (5)
14 Postage item (3)
16 Like dismal skies (4)
17 Driving club (7)
18 "Mamma Mia!" setting (6)
19 Stomach problem (7)
23 Parisian's nicety (5)
26 Part of a French conjugation (4)
28 Longest-running current TV drama (3)
29 Photo showing just the face (8)
30 Jeremy of "Suburgatory" (5)

Down

1 On the modest side (8)
2 Golf course scurriers (5)
3 Arena income (4)
5 English offshoot (8)
6 Breezed (6)
7 Fast plane (3)
9 Toyota pickup (6)
10 Hide behind words (5)
11 Levied as a tax (7)
13 A luge driver might wear one (7)
15 Music's Faith (5)
18 Like moussaka and souvlaki (5)
20 Bit of citrus rind in a drink (5)
21 Shelters (4)
22 Sound reduced by carpeting (4)
24 Reduce (4)
25 F.S. has ___ hundreds of hits (4)
27 Kind of shelter (3)

CROSSWORD 06

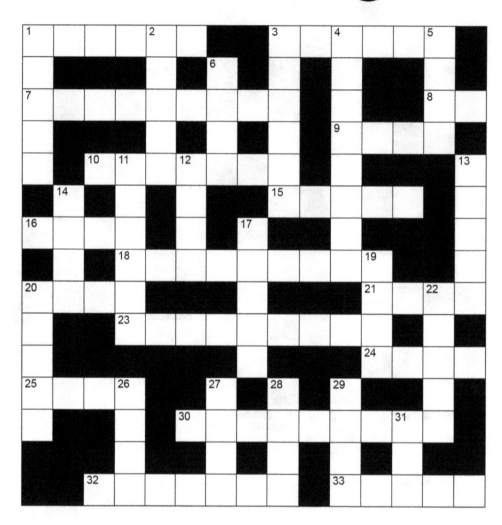

Across

1   Things towed along towpaths (6)
3   Renewal target (6)
7   Scold. (9)
8   TV format (2)
9   California's San __ Obispo (4)
10 ___ Stone (brand of language-learning software) (7)
15 Ben's mother Anne (5)
16 One over the eight (4)
18 Drill leaders (9)
20 Route (4)
21 "Chop-chop!" on a memo (4)
23 Sound system staples (9)
24 MDs' ASAP (4)
25 Peer group? (4)
30 Place to eat, drink and log in (9)
32 Sots (7)
33 Pieman's wares (5)

Down

1   Wax-and-dye design (5)
2   "OMG!," quaintly (5)
3   Batman's domain (6)
4   Showing great joy (8)
5   '60s protest singer Phil (4)
6   Character set (4)
11 "Hold that thought" (6)
12 "Oh, when will they __ learn?" (4)
13 John B, in song (5)
14 One of a Hindu trinity (4)
17 Aluminum, for one (5)
19 Cause for a child's scolding (4)
20 1.0567 liquid quarts. (5)
22 "What's in ___" (5)
26 Artsy Big Apple neighborhood (4)
27 Scot's "since" (4)
28 Puts in type (4)
29 "___ in gloves catches no mice" (4)
31 Douglas ___ tree (3)

CROSSWORD 07

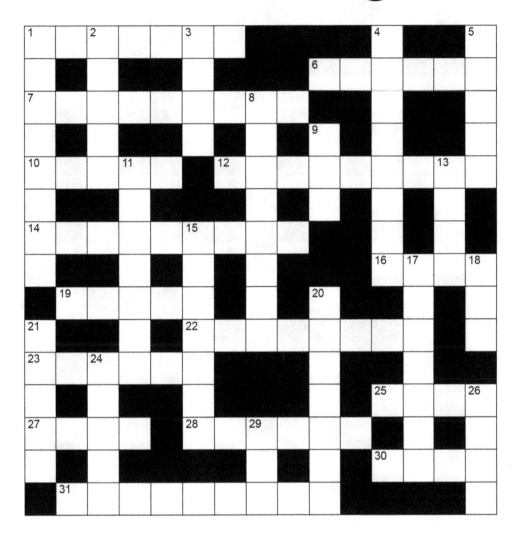

Across

1   Coastal scavenger (7)
6   Braggart (6)
7   Largest snakes in the world (9)
10 Punch back instinctively (5)
12 Sully (9)
14 Watches secretly (9)
16 Himalayan that you probably wouldn't want to pet (4)
19 ___ cavity (5)
22 Like many interviews (8)
23 Navy (6)
25 Eat like a mouse (4)
27 Emergency CB channel (4)
28 Lions, to Bantus (6)
30 Middle East country where "Argo" is largely set (4)
31 Lace into (9)

Down

1   TV host Ryan (8)
2   Half of an African capital (5)
3   TV host Jay ____ (4)
4   Peasantry's opposite (8)
5   Music's Shaw (5)
8   Draft locale (8)
9   Quaint complaint (3)
11 1990's White House occupant (7)
13 Horse race pace (4)
15 Dumps (on) (7)
17 Mother of Richard I and John (7)
18 Suffix with "consumer" (3)
20 Seeing someone, say (7)
21 Actor Michael (5)
24 Nourishment of divine origin (5)
26 Disappeared (4)
29 Kingston Trio hit of 1959 (3)

CROSSWORD 08

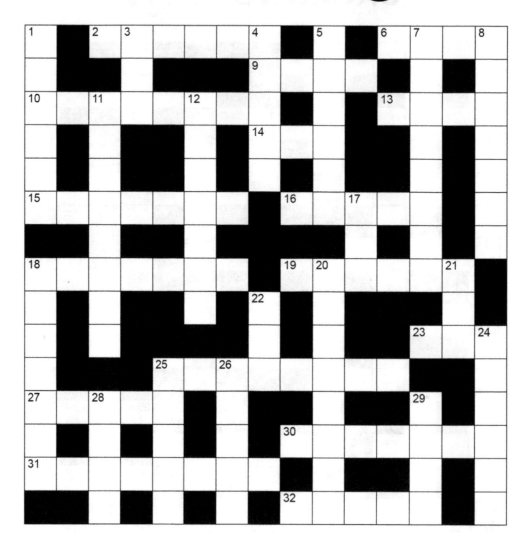

Across

2   City in Montana (6)
6   Dial ___ (4)
9   Things that can be rolled over, for short (4)
10 Transferral to specialist (8)
13 Prefix meaning bone (4)
14 Over-easy breakfast item? (3)
15 Spreadsheet figures (7)
16 Daughter of Queen Juliana of the Netherlands (5)
18 "My Many Colored Days" author (7)
19 "Hell Freezes Over" band (6)
23 3 for an FG, e.g. (3)
25 Friend of Henry Miller (8)
27 Stress, cigarettes, handing car keys to your teen, e.g. (5)
30 Yahtzee prop (7)
31 ___ hour (crisis) (8)
32 Wire (5)

Down

1   It's a deal! (6)
3   Increase (3)
4   Needed a doctor (5)
5   Nag (6)
7   Out-of-date (8)
8   Wee she on a lea (7)
11 Potpourri of well-known airs (8)
12 Gear shift. (7)
17 Neighbor of Fr. (3)
18 Command (7)
20 ___ Mountains of Italy (8)
21 Undertake, with "out" (3)
22 Hawaiian shirt go-with (3)
24 Show impatience with (6)
25 Urn contents (5)
26 Take ___ (lose a bundle) (5)
28 Nightfalls (4)
29 Vaper's purchase, for short (4)

CROSSWORD 09

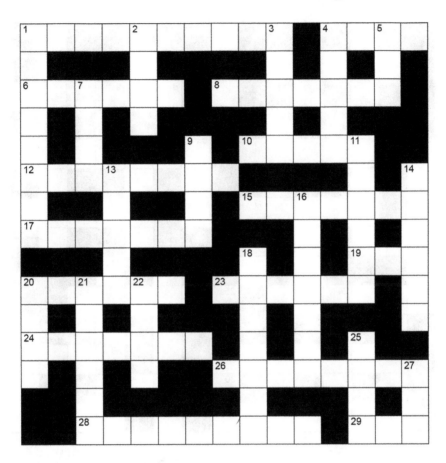

Across

1 Underground employees (10)
4 Mask part (4)
6 Shareholders, for instance (6)
8 Gladden (7)
10 Vertical, to a sailor (5)
12 License requirements, perhaps (8)
15 Receivers' counterparts (7)
17 Dog shelters (7)
19 Site of the incus (3)
20 Priests' vestments (6)
23 Tells the po-po about (6)
24 Glance given to troublemakers (7)
26 Previn and Bernstein, for two (8)
28 Motorcycle demos, e.g. (9)
29 Moo ___ pork (Chinese menu food) (3)

Down

1 1966 hit for the Capitols (8)
2 What happy concertgoers want (4)
3 Abrupt (5)
4 Maker of the iComfort mattress (5)
5 Babysitter's problem (3)
7 Schnozzle (4)
9 "How sweet ---!" (4)
11 ___ Ivory Wayans (6)
13 Gin complement (5)
14 2005 National League champions (6)
16 Hard things to hit (7)
18 Pale and worn (7)
20 Dazed and confused (4)
21 Words of self-congratulation (6)
22 Hall _Oates "Don't ___ think about it, say no go" (4)
25 Personal reserve funds, for short (4)
27 Yugoslav river, to Germans (3)

CROSSWORD 10

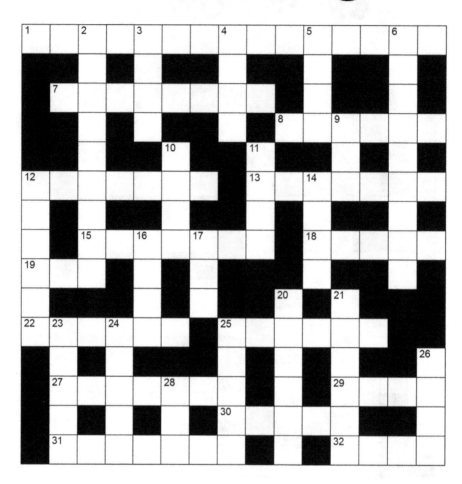

Across

1 Kin of a user's manual (15)
7 Fought off (8)
8 Lose one's temper (6)
12 Not a main route (7)
13 Causes (oneself) to be cherished (7)
15 Like some experimental cars (7)
18 "Slammin' Sam" (5)
19 Three in a season (3)
22 "I'm all ears!" (6)
25 Like most crossword puzzles (6)
27 Front porch (7)
29 Riviera shade (4)
30 "Paradise Lost" villain (5)
31 Plant plight (7)
32 Gene's director in "Laura" (4)

Down

2 Border collies, notably (9)
3 Saucier's concern (4)
4 Sycamore or oak (4)
5 Thing sometimes dropped (4)
6 Mr. Fixit (9)
9 'BTW' part (3)
10 Viscount's peer (4)
11 Flock's locale (4)
12 A high-level meeting? (6)
14 Disrespect another rocker, slang (4)
16 It may be filtered into its own folder (4)
17 Emergency copter operation (3)
20 Precipitate (6)
21 FDR's middle name (6)
23 Young conger (5)
24 Slowly, musically (5)
25 Some bread (5)
26 Craft that crossed through Clashing Rocks (4)
28 Repeated word in a Herodotus quote (3)

CROSSWORD 11

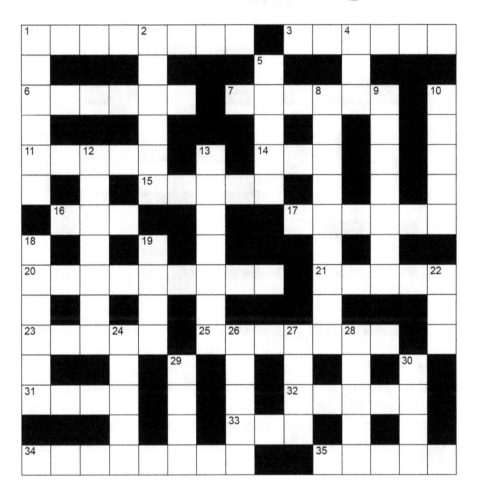

Across

1 Famed Concord family (8)
3 One who's suffering (6)
6 Auditory canal blocker (6)
7 Sets free (6)
11 One in a bottle (5)
14 Like Capp's Abner (3)
15 March around camp, e.g. (5)
16 Give it one's all (3)
17 Apple processing plant (6)
20 Ruler's role (9)
21 Stale-smelling (5)
23 "Goodnight ___" (1950 hit) (5)
25 Polar bears, e.g. (7)
31 Hide, but not hair (4)
32 It adds luster (5)
33 Psychoanalysis topic (3)
34 Flavoring liquids (8)
35 Sleeping place (5)

Down

1 What fuel provides (6)
2 Desexed (6)
4 Hex- ender (3)
5 " . . . and ___ a good night!" (5)
8 Education financing company, familiarly (9)
9 Ones concealing their aims (7)
10 One may be tucked (5)
12 Record an audio book (7)
13 Send packing (7)
18 Inbox buildup (6)
19 Frank Herbert saga (4)
22 Dist. measures (3)
24 NFL player (5)
26 Places for gutters (5)
27 New kids' block since 1958 (4)
28 Major French river (5)
29 "Peter Pan" ticker (4)
30 Step toward a JD (4)

CROSSWORD 12

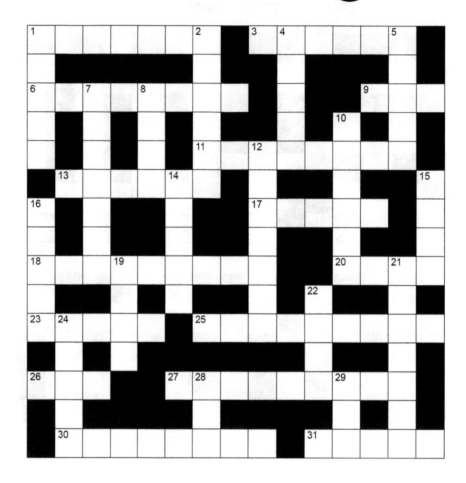

Across

1 Ways (7)
3 Sends through the air (6)
6 Poisonous salt (8)
9 Go out, as a fire (3)
11 Steer elsewhere (8)
13 Some antelopes (6)
17 Touches on (5)
18 Title song of a 1970 Van Morrison album (9)
20 Car-pooler's need (4)
23 Useful parts of the alphabet. (5)
25 Retire for the night (informal) (9)
26 Cheer in Toledo (3)
27 They don't provide outlets (9)
30 Bird's footwear (8)
31 Lizards of West (5)

Down

1 Concession ___ (5)
2 Fauns (6)
4 Mystery-story ingredient (5)
5 Typewriter key (5)
7 Aggressive, moody type, they say (7)
8 Clueless "Skyrim" player, e.g. (4)
10 One targeting the quarterback (6)
12 Forensic activity (7)
14 Bygone Apple messenger (5)
15 Swede's neighbor (4)
16 Buccaneers' base (5)
19 Certain G.I.'s (4)
21 Lowest lake (7)
22 Does, e.g. (4)
24 "American Psycho" novelist Bret Easton ___ (5)
28 Take, as a drug (3)
29 Caliph or pugilist (3)

CROSSWORD 13

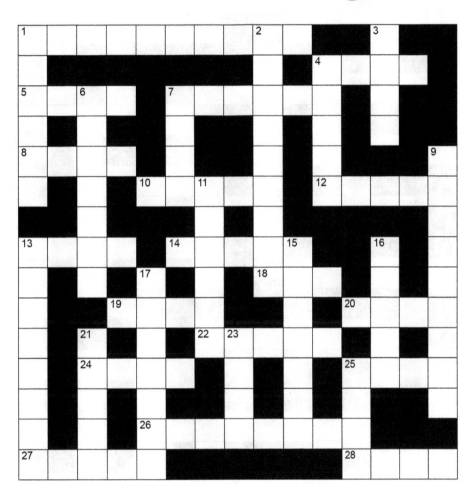

Across

1 Two-way journeys (10)
4 Thing you oughtn't do (4)
5 Usually unread email (4)
7 Bilingual woman, maybe (6)
8 Drew's "50 First Dates" costar (4)
10 Agitated (5)
12 Banker's client (5)
13 Holding for a bank dep. (4)
14 Shuts loudly, as doors (5)
18 Leggy runner (3)
19 It might be topped with guacamole (4)
20 Tests for srs. (4)
22 Undivided (5)
24 Major Air France terminus (4)
25 King of Siam's love (4)
26 Post-tragedy joking, e.g. (8)
27 Worcester, e.g. (5)
28 Not just brown (4)

Down

1 "Where is the ___ cook?" (6)
2 Viewing period (9)
3 Cause of many days off (4)
4 It's not nice to call them (5)
6 Miser's motif. (7)
7 Favor a "th" sound (4)
9 Bridge dream (9)
11 Having a sickly coloring (6)
13 Coats with a protective oxide (8)
15 Grinning symbols (7)
16 Eaten at (5)
17 Drop zone? (7)
21 Actress in "Anger Management," 2003 (5)
23 Offend(ed) (4)
25 Guinness of stage (4)

CROSSWORD 14

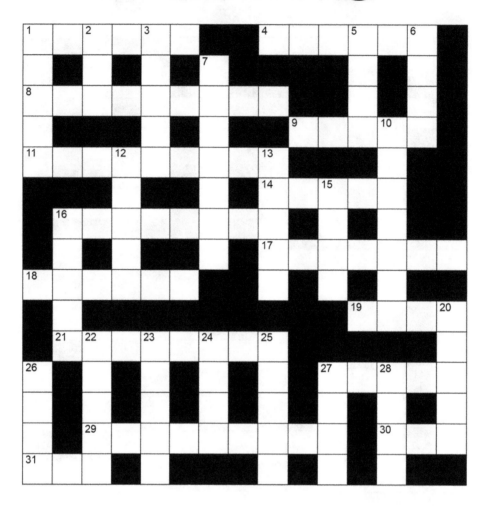

Across

1 Acid found in yeast (6)
4 Uses a teapot (6)
8 Amore from Anita Baker, 1986 (9)
9 Old sitcom about a single mom working at a Phoenix diner (5)
11 Saint Petersburg, until 1991 (9)
14 Tie the knot quickly (5)
16 Status (8)
17 Pitch (7)
18 Bit of body art (6)
19 Snakes on some Egyptian artifacts (4)
21 Comes after The Police's "De Do Do Do" (8)
27 Caine title role (5)
29 Result of flying the coop? (9)
30 Army sack? (3)
31 "___ Man in Havana" (3)

Down

1 Kind of decongestant (5)
2 It's poured in pints (3)
3 "Back ___ minutes" (shop-door sign) (5)
5 Chatelaine's case (4)
6 Label designation (4)
7 Deliver or else (7)
10 They're made by origami artists (7)
12 Clarifying phrase usually abbreviated (5)
13 Acta (5)
15 Soccer stadium cries (4)
16 Geometric pattern (5)
20 Form of clay pigeon shooting (5)
22 Basel-born mathematician (5)
23 Do as the Romans do, so to speak (5)
24 Eagle's roost (4)
25 "Li'l" one (5)
26 Longtime maker of the Magic 8 Ball (4)
27 Team-player liaisons (4)
28 Book category (4)

CROSSWORD 15

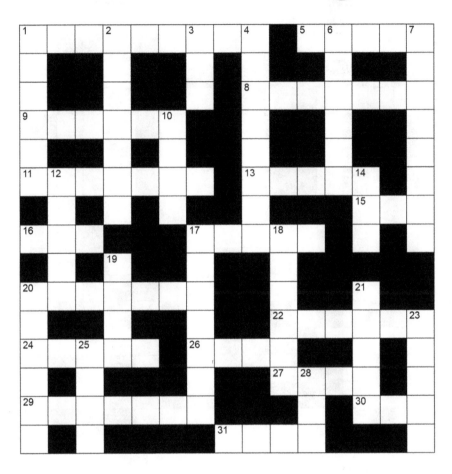

Across

1 Bachelor party entertainment (9)
5 Big trucks (5)
8 Albert Payson Terhune book (7)
9 Tommy Hilfiger's New York birthplace (6)
11 "Why don't we!" (7)
13 Airborne toy (5)
15 Dogpatch's Daisy __ (3)
16 North Slope yield (3)
17 Rich apparel (5)
20 Heavenly higher-ups, in Christianity (7)
22 In the buff (6)
24 Keep an __ (5)
26 Knight-time story (4)
27 Make hourly (4)
29 Doc wannabes (7)
30 Bluto's was 0.0 in "Animal House" (3)
31 It's broken off (4)

Down

1 Vivacious (6)
2 The Ten Commandments   director (7)
3 Get all lovey-dovey (3)
4 Steakhouse feature (8)
6 Turkish mountain (6)
7 Take a vacation tour (8)
10 Cumulus lead-in (4)
12 Person absent from home or country (5)
14 Punk rock genre (3)
17 Transfers, as legal rights (7)
18 Crafty (6)
19 Military's mottled clothing, for short (4)
20 Hibernates (6)
21 Jive talkin' (5)
23 No-kick coffee (5)
25 Actress famously known for hitting the bottle? (4)
28 Eggleton or Meighen, familiarly (3)

CROSSWORD 16

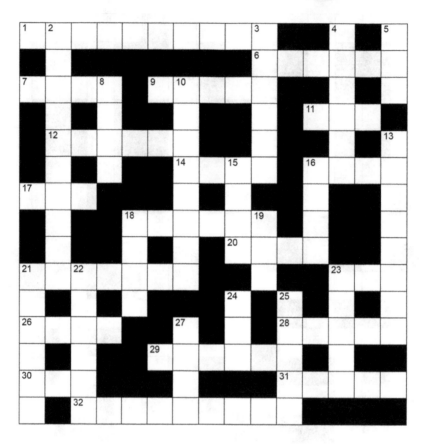

Across

1 Blue-eyed feline (10)
6 Recovers the road (6)
7 Longest book of the Book of Mormon (4)
9 Pancake of Southwest (5)
11 Proposition vote (3)
12 "Venus and Adonis" painter (6)
14 Ocular sphincter (4)
16 Priest at Lhasa (4)
17 Republican gp. (3)
18 Made more powerful, with "up" (6)
20 Runner-up to Achilles (4)
21 Word with "lobe" or "assault" (7)
23 Egyptian deity (3)
26 Colorado tribe members (4)
28 Story theme (5)
29 Minister (6)
30 Number of players on a beach volleyball team (3)
31 Detective role for Beatty (5)
32 Treat, as meat (9)

Down

2 Unemployed renter? (10)
3 Idiosyncrasies (6)
4 Eponym of Gdansk's airport (6)
5 Chicago-to-Atlanta direction (3)
8 Greek Church pulpit (4)
10 Surplus amount (8)
13 Poor sport (8)
15 Furniture chain with "Bjursta" and "Ingatorp" dining tables (4)
16 Medici family pope (4)
18 Bristle (4)
19 Wedding entertainers (3)
21 Describing a rich cake. (6)
22 Cat the margay takes after (6)
23 ___ notte (5)
24 Platoon members, briefly (3)
25 Congressman Fascell (5)
27 Where the congregation congregates (4)

CROSSWORD 17

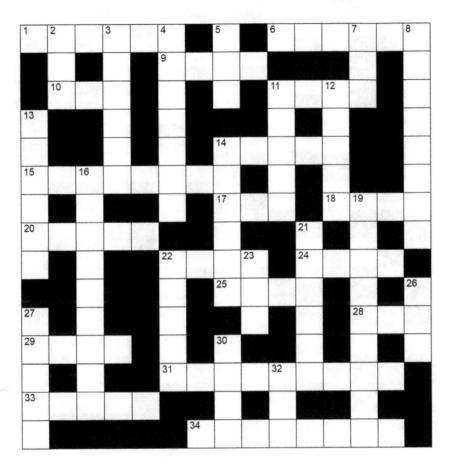

Across

1   Lady-in-waiting in "Othello" (6)
6   It cuts wood along the grain (6)
9   Space between the eye and the bill (4)
10 Contact info spec. (3)
11 Time spent in line, seemingly (4)
14 Athenian center (5)
15 U. S. poet (8)
17 Atlanta-based sta. (3)
18 High guy (4)
20 Maker of "the plow that broke the Plains" (5)
22 Title role for Leslie Caron (4)
24 Harper of Hollywood (4)
25 Enough to count on one hand (4)
28 Worked on a sub, say (3)
29 Athletic field (4)
31 Classic Girl Scout cookies (9)
33 Land unit, in Canada (5)
34 They're spent in airports (8)

Down

2   Comedian Howard (3)
3   The Edict of Worms condemned him (6)
4   Yearbook of forecasts (7)
5   Questionable Refund Program org. (3)
7   Shining example? (3)
8   Space for home projects, e.g. (8)
11 Celebes oxen (5)
12 "The Oracle of ___" (Warren Buffett nickname) (5)
13 Winter wear (6)
14 Big name among Huns (6)
16 Foes' home base (9)
19 Desire (9)
21 Confessor's confession (6)
22 As high as you can possibly go (5)
23 "___ were you" (3)
26 Word in a bride's bio (3)
27 Reef predator (5)
30 Makeup of some insulating sheets (4)
32 Field sound (3)

CROSSWORD 18

Across

1 Singer Peter (6)
6 Blind ___ bat (3)
8 Old string players (7)
10 Start of a promise (3)
11 Back payments (7)
12 Leave runny on the inside, say (8)
13 Old-fashioned writing tool (6)
15 1959 Fiestas hit (6)
19 Flout (4)
20 Sun shunners (8)
22 Gets brown (4)
24 Vitamin-B complex member (6)
25 Gas in commercial lights (4)
26 Go very slowly (4)
28 Dead (7)
30 Singer who is a judge on "World of Dance" (4)
31 "You can say that again!" (6)
32 Size that's usually perfect for printing crosswords, but often not for mine because I tend to write really long clues and you might need more space, for short (3)

Down

1 Some MOMA painters (7)
2 Undemocratic law (5)
3 Little kid's words after finishing a meal (7)
4 Baseball play (5)
5 Old Russian noble (4)
7 Muscle cramps, e.g. (6)
9 Warned, in a way (9)
14 Autobiography of 47A (8)
16 Fanciful (9)
17 School areas with high ceilings (4)
18 Separated (into portions) (7)
21 Early toddlerhood (6)
23 Cathode's opposite (5)
27 Acronym for the four major show biz awards (4)
29 Guest's bed (3)

CROSSWORD 19

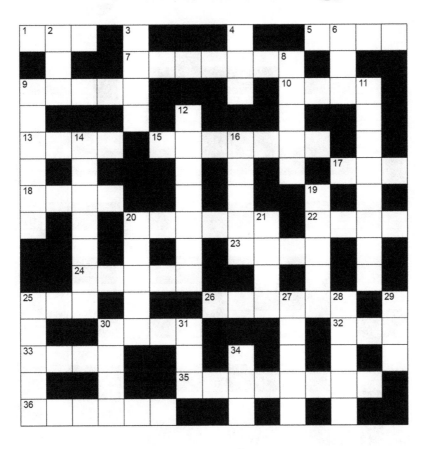

Across

1 Song on an album (3)
5 Per ____ (4)
7 Poet Wallace ___ (7)
9 Austen's Jane Fairfax, for one (5)
10 Yankee until '16 (4)
13 Like a door with a foot in it (4)
15 Man. (7)
17 Faulkner title start (3)
18 Senator Vinick's portrayer on "The West Wing" (4)
20 Kazakhs and Koreans (6)
22 Like pinnacle of career (4)
23 Tiny bit of matter (4)
24 One who's doomed (5)
25 Zap (3)
26 Distribute widely (6)
30 Any moment (4)
32 "Hip, hip, Jorge!" (3)
33 Coating on a clunker (4)
35 2004 MLS Cup winner (8)
36 Beetle of note (6)

Down

2 Academic inst. in the Ocean State (3)
3 Like many college textbooks (4)
4 Word of assent (3)
6 Alike (3)
8 Like most pickles and pretzels (5)
9 Classic sports videogame with exaggerated player moves (6)
11 Valets, at times (8)
12 Gamal Abdel Nasser, notably (7)
14 Still a little firm (7)
16 She worked with Asta (5)
19 Place of Mead studies (5)
20 Hersey's 'A Bell for --' (5)
21 Restaurant review symbol (4)
25 Up, on most maps (5)
27 PC letters etc. (5)
28 Kind of sole (5)
29 Twisty fish (3)
30 Much-used pencil, e.g. (4)
31 "The Simpsons" neighborino (3)
34 The ultimate early riser (3)

CROSSWORD 20

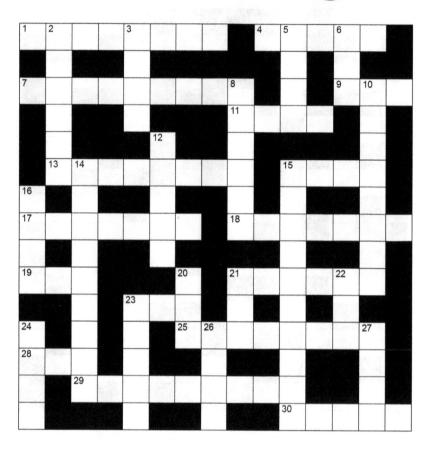

Across

1 Islets of Langerhans locale (8)
4 Drink container (5)
7 Baying? (9)
9 Colon half (3)
11 First player whose HR was reviewed (and upheld) by umpires using instant replay (4)
13 Workout aftermath, often (8)
15 Road hazards (4)
17 Verdun and Vicksburg. (7)
18 Former Eli Lilly barbiturate brand (7)
19 Descendant of Aaron, in the Bible (3)
21 Bearlike (6)
23 ___-med student (3)
25 Bit of ingenuity (8)
28 ___ World (3)
29 Post-wedding party (9)
30 Outing at the mall? (5)

Down

2 Kind of brief in court (6)
3 Things to exterminate, to many (4)
5 Celebrity who testified at the 2005 Michael Jackson trial (4)
6 Grass roll (3)
8 Authoritative assurances (6)
10 Corporate gadfly's purchase, maybe (8)
12 Attach to (5)
14 Feature of a Pacific canoe (9)
15 Booms' opposites (10)
16 Vowel-rich woodwind (4)
20 Age of a fourth- or fifth-grader (3)
21 2015 World Cup winner (3)
22 90° from ESE (3)
23 Bit (5)
24 Tunnel creator (4)
26 Sermon finisher? (4)
27 Frank known for her World War II diary (4)

CROSSWORD 21

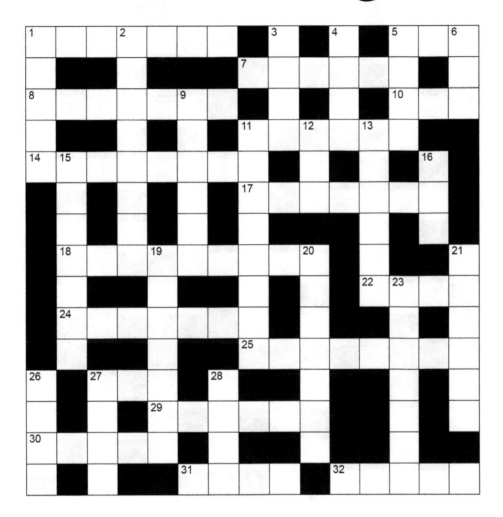

Across

1 Unknown by (7)
5 Organization for Rory McIlroy (3)
7 Ones with crossed arms, traditionally (6)
8 Future bureaucrat's major, briefly (7)
10 "___ Popular Man," Cohan song (3)
11 "Easy to clean," in ads (6)
14 Disgust (8)
17 Distortion (7)
18 Portrayal (9)
22 Grammy subcategory of Gospel (4)
24 Like the figure formed by the three circled letters in the upper left (7)
25 Fault line? (8)
27 Penn's Pocono ____ (3)
29 Introduce during a newscast, say (6)
30 Roger formerly of Fox News (5)
31 1930s film dog (4)
32 2011 outbreak bacteria (5)

Down

1 Ski resort southwest of Vail (5)
2 Discharge (8)
3 Move, in Realtor lingo (4)
4 Threatening (4)
5 Letters from Greece (4)
6 Org. for codebreakers (3)
9 Like sandpaper (6)
11 Bit of daily reading (8)
12 Leave scratches on, e.g. (3)
13 Penguins' footwear (6)
15 Formal talk (7)
16 Judy Garland, ___ Frances Gumm (3)
19 Removes from the exchange (7)
20 Reflective opal (7)
21 "Citizen Kane" actor Everett (6)
23 SeaWorld venue (7)
26 Reinforcement for a collar (4)
27 Pinochle tactic (4)
28 Org. that delivers (4)

CROSSWORD 22

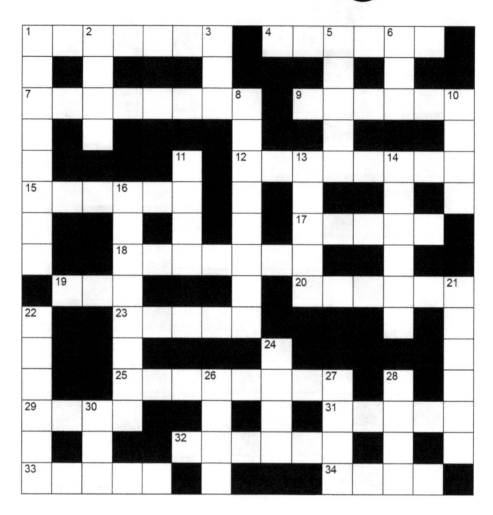

Across

1 Hankers (7)
4 Transfer abroad (6)
7 Vivaldi opera based on "The Decameron" (8)
9 Traveling and performing (6)
12 "The Day Dream" painter (8)
15 Rector's charge (6)
17 Celestial flare-ups (5)
18 Producer of the Keystone Cops films (7)
19 Slow down, in mus. (3)
20 Montezuma's subjects (6)
23 "___ of Varnish" (C. P. Snow novel) (5)
25 Japan's Feast of ___ (8)
29 Roget's listings (4)
31 Piece that teaches technique (5)
32 Greeting with a bow (6)
33 _____ Owl (5)
34 Unwrinkler (4)

Down

1 Most memorable moment (8)
2 Marina mooring (4)
3 "The Other Normals" author Vizzini (3)
5 Fragrant trees (5)
6 Orson Welles's old studio (3)
8 Wartime signal (8)
10 Bug killer brand (4)
11 Consequently. (4)
13 Chimney guy (5)
14 Bartered (6)
16 Hooks up an appliance (8)
21 Went up alone (6)
22 Construction site apparatuses (6)
24 Judith Blegen offering (4)
26 Warp-resistant wood (4)
27 It may make a big haul (4)
28 City in NW Spain (4)
30 Art movement prefix (3)

CROSSWORD 23

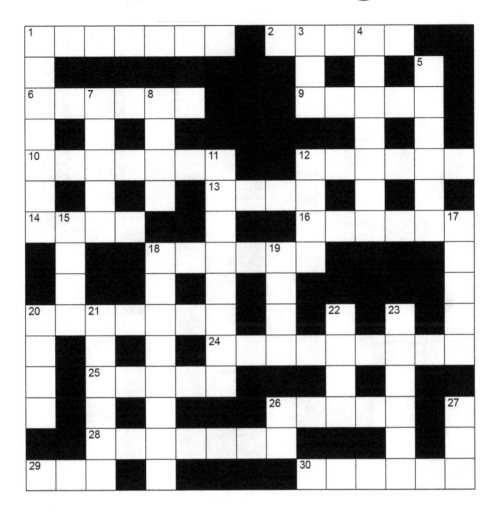

Across

1 Bother or difficulty (7)
2 Military standings, e.g. (5)
6 Passport office, e.g. (6)
9 Before (5)
10 Accumulated by the pope? (7)
12 Twinings competitor (6)
13 "Tell Mama" singer James (4)
14 Spin (4)
16 Eel type (6)
18 Latch again, as a door (6)
20 Bees (7)
24 Beach wear (9)
25 In a separate place (5)
26 Shoe strips (5)
28 Done better at retail (7)
29 Negating word (3)
30 Panorama (6)

Down

1 What one vanishes into? (7)
3 Thing involved in a phone tap? (3)
4 Chenoweth of Broadway's "Wicked" (7)
5 Land of feta (6)
7 Lose a lap? (5)
8 Polo goal (4)
11 Reduced in status (8)
12 Small fastener (4)
15 "There ___ I in T-E-A-M" (4)
17 Leghorns' lodgings (5)
18 Practical ones (8)
19 Take it on the ___ (be badly hurt) (4)
20 Head high (4)
21 Hue and cry (6)
22 Name in the "Fargo" credits (4)
23 Infant's outfit (6)
27 Denver clock reading (3)

CROSSWORD 24

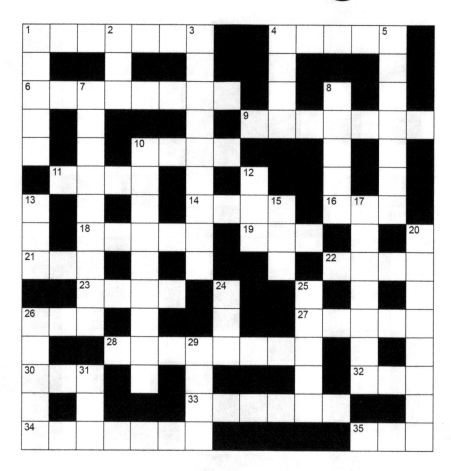

Across

1　Radio adjunct (7)
4　"In my wildest dreams" (5)
6　Eau de ___ (8)
9　Professions (7)
10　Old sweetheart? (4)
11　Ali the woodcutter (4)
14　"___ in the Morning" (radio program) (4)
16　Ike's monogram (3)
18　Bothered incessantly (5)
19　"Lord, is ___?" (3)
21　Truck weight unit (3)
22　Brand that's canned (4)
23　Lamb or karate (4)
26　Bread for a ham sandwich, often (3)
27　Terse denial (5)
28　Nightwear (8)
30　Had a Presidential role (3)
32　"Who ___?" (New Orleans slang) (3)
33　Site of an 1862 Union victory (6)
34　Pigeons (7)
35　Fruit Roll-___ (3)

Down

1　What comes before all? (5)
2　Avocado accompanier in some rolls (3)
3　Beingness or existence (9)
4　State that holds the first presidential caucuses (4)
5　Clairol product (7)
7　Equilibratory (9)
8　Biblical king of Judea (5)
10　Far from frilly (9)
12　Word before "juris" or "generis" (3)
13　Like some kisses (3)
15　Cardinal's cap monogram (3)
17　Took out (7)
20　Miss Young and others (8)
24　Tuna steak tuna (3)
25　January, in Rio (5)
26　Acting credits (5)
29　One with "the delicate air" (4)
31　Lovebirds, e.g. (3)

CROSSWORD 25

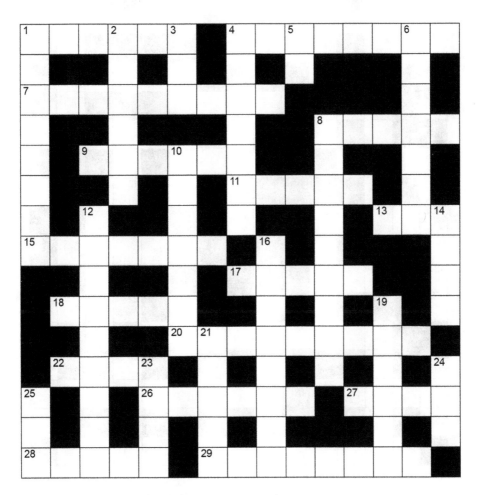

Across

1   Miranda July, e.g. (6)
4   Circle graph (8)
7   "You made your point" (9)
8   Gives advance warning (5)
9   Existing at birth (6)
11 Paige who provided the voice of Belle in "Beauty and the Beast" (5)
13 Dr. Fiona Hill's former grp. (3)
15 Victims of many triple slaps (7)
17 Tinkerbell (5)
18 Pair of drum-kit cymbals (5)
20 You'll need one for your flat (9)
22 Yacht's docking place (4)
26 Simian snack (6)
27 Cape buffalo (4)
28 Gets the consolation prize (5)
29 Church features (8)

Down

1   Report card notation (8)
2   Meteorological event (6)
3   Dark 'n' Stormy ingredient (3)
4   August birthstone (7)
5   Jovanovski, for one (2)
6   Summer fare on TV (7)
8   Cruelty (9)
10 Snakes' intakes (7)
12 Ward heelers (9)
14 Schlep (4)
16 Jack who wrote the lyrics to "Tenderly" (8)
19 Carrier Dome team (6)
21 Loblollies and larches (5)
23 Scorecard entries (4)
24 Spray on a pan (3)
25 Salt on the Seine (3)

CROSSWORD 26

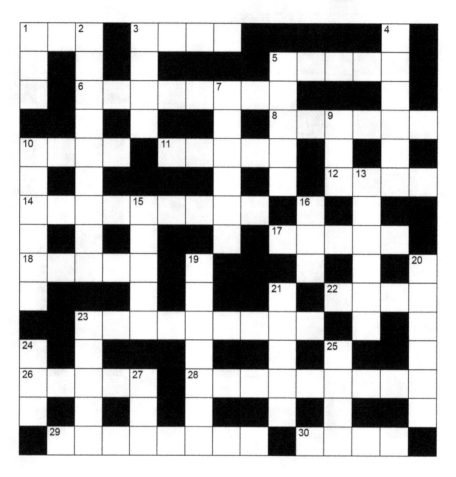

Across

1   '80s hit "___ Kommissar" (3)
3   At leisure (4)
5   Just-baked pies have one (5)
6   ... HIT A RA(W)(N)(E)RVE, ARE (W)(E)(N)OT
    ME(N)(W)(E) ARE DEVO, and SPOK(E)(N)(W)ORD (8)
8   Game often played with a 24-card deck (6)
10 "Thirty days ___ September ..." (4)
11 City where Pixar's "Ratatouille" is set (5)
12 Title VII enforcer (4)
14 Franz Liszt, e.g. / Didn't go straight, maybe [split] (9)
17 Inquire again (5)
18 Inventor of alternating current (5)
22 Signal farewell (4)
23 Half a noted comedy duo (9)
26 Wounds (5)
28 Encoder (9)
29 Loathes (8)
30 Pre-twentysomething (4)

Down

1   West ___ Moines (3)
2   Significant music industry market, nowadays (9)
3   Young Bambi (4)
4   Arrangement of locks (6)
5   "You __ lucky!" (sore loser's remark) (5)
7   Cathedral city on the River Wear (6)
9   Co., in Cherbourg (3)
10 Parts of a drummer's kit (6)
13 Words with "pie" or "1-2-3" (6)
15 At full speed, poetically (5)
16 Luthor in "Superman" (3)
19 Gradual absorption (7)
20 Moth-deterrent woods (6)
21 "Iliad" king (5)
23 Onyx relative (5)
24 Abbr. in a personal ad (3)
25 Having skill or strength (4)
27 Routine letters (3)

CROSSWORD 27

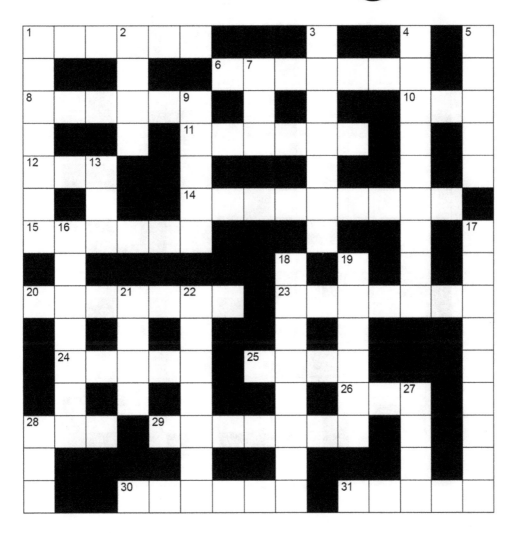

Across

1　Product of erosion (6)
6　"Tight shorts," said the boxer ___ (7)
8　Tough phrases for foreigners (6)
10　Actress Carides of "My Big Fat Greek Wedding 2" (3)
11　Worn things (6)
12　Univ. at Columbus (3)
14　Leader of an 1831 slave rebellion (9)
15　Keanu's 'Speed' co-star (6)
20　Most picayune (7)
23　Provider of underground entertainment? (7)
24　Not germane (5)
25　Sow's supper (4)
26　"Fab" attachment (3)
28　Old Turkish commander (3)
29　Breathe (7)
30　Sneaker feature (6)
31　"Get ___!" ('90s catchphrase) (5)

Down

1　Destructive (7)
2　Pet bat in TV's "The Munsters" (4)
3　Support (7)
4　Roaring Twenties, for example (9)
5　Desert Storm plane acronym (5)
7　Ben, in a film (3)
9　Hot house? (5)
13　First "Enterprise" airer (3)
16　With a lasting quality (7)
17　Confuse (9)
18　Designer's autumn offerings (8)
19　Plain plain (6)
21　Apple Store purchase (4)
22　English hunters (7)
27　Military vet (4)
28　Louvre exhibits, collectively (3)

CROSSWORD 28

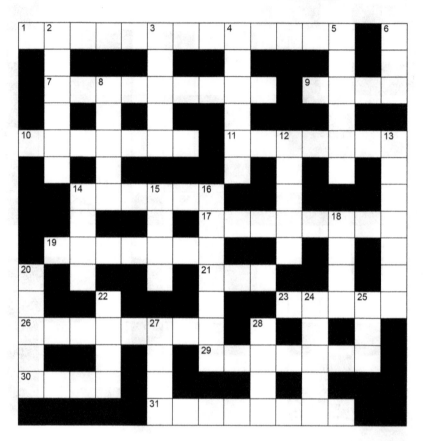

Across

1 Speaker of the quote (13)
7 Tax write-off (9)
9 She "Begins" with Counting Crows on "August _Everything After" (4)
10 Chilling, so to speak (7)
11 "We did it!" (7)
14 Sheath (6)
17 Gorgeous guys (8)
19 Prosperous periods (7)
21 Small mound (3)
23 Dirk DeJong's nickname in a 1924 novel (5)
26 Michigan city (8)
29 Romanian tennis great (7)
30 Body opening? (4)
31 One with a burning passion (8)

Down

2 Lipton product, as marketed in some European countries (6)
3 Small thicket (5)
4 Like a copse (6)
5 Coors Field locale (6)
6 RR destination (3)
8 Virus carrier (5)
12 Complete copy (5)
13 Being disrespectful to (7)
14 Beholds (4)
15 Where online shoppers place bids (4)
16 Part of E.S.T. (7)
18 Kosovo resident (4)
20 German child's hero (5)
22 Main ingredient (4)
24 Grad student's rituals (5)
25 Adopted "South Park" sibling (3)
27 Ali ____ (4)
28 " ___ alternative ..." (4)

CROSSWORD 29

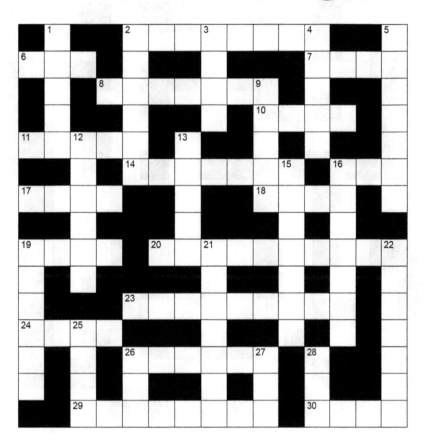

Across

2 Unfading flower (8)
6 Financial services company with a lion logo (3)
7 Molding with a double curve (4)
8 Tooth tissue (7)
10 Glance impolitely (4)
11 Medicinal tropical plant (5)
14 Opening (7)
16 Aretha Franklin "___ Saw" (3)
17 Cuzco people (4)
18 Footsteps-in-an-empty-hallway sound (4)
19 Readied to drive, with "up" (4)
20 Phrase before "here I come" (10)
23 Yeses from bosses (9)
24 "Not so fast!" (4)
26 Under an elm (6)
29 Historically significant symbol (8)
30 Mean, lowdown sorts (4)

Down

1 Word that can precede "city" or "tube" (5)
2 Punta ___, city in Chile (6)
3 Vice squad action (4)
4 "Iliad" poet (5)
5 Reappear on stage (7)
9 Hypocritical pejorative when used by millionaire senators born into political families (5)
12 Go too far (6)
13 Carlo beginning (5)
15 Nimble circus performer (7)
16 Blankety-blank type (7)
19 Tool for laying cement (6)
21 Shorten (7)
22 The Beatles and others (7)
25 Home of Utah Valley State College (4)
26 Data theft target (3)
27 Mar.-Nov. hours (3)
28 Former govt. agency (3)

CROSSWORD 30

Across

2 "___ Men" (2010 Jude Law movie) (4)
4 French individuals (4)
6 Uncle ___ of "Seinfeld" (3)
10 Grueling workplace, so to speak (8)
11 Running a temperature (3)
12 ___ Energy (Red Bull rival) (3)
14 Like a student's D (4)
16 Apple-pie bakers (4)
17 Stat for Zach Britton (4)
18 Big Board initials (3)
21 Narrated (7)
23 Birth state of skier Picabo Street (5)
24 Hit a batter (4)
25 Author Wister of "The Virginian" (4)
26 "Angels _Demons" antimatter org. (4)
28 Beguile (9)
30 "Severn Meadows" poet Gurney (4)
31 Patterns of small pieces (7)
32 Word in many songs sung in December (4)
33 "Primary Colors" author, for short (4)

Down

1 Disco doctor (9)
3 Most soldiers in a battle scene, probably (6)
5 Rear-___ (traffic mishap) (5)
7 State of hate (5)
8 Religion of hundreds of millions (5)
9 Check out (7)
13 Drinking bash (11)
15 How buzzkills end things (9)
19 Drain (4)
20 George Sanders role (5)
21 Orange-breasted bird (5)
22 Persistent follower (8)
26 Group of witches (5)
27 Gerald and Hodges (4)
29 Jimmy Buffett "You're better off with ___" (4)

CROSSWORD 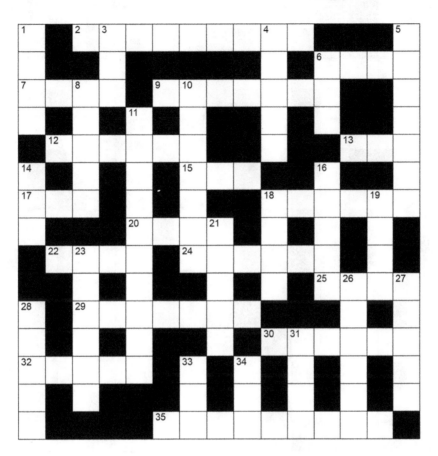31

Across

2 Hold fellow at the club entrance? (9)
6 Young toon explorer (4)
7 Mussolini's title (4)
9 One of Einstein's fortes (7)
12 Large bowl (6)
13 Top-blowing emotion (3)
15 "General" on Chinese menus (3)
17 "Pirates of the Caribbean (3)
18 Kind of water or training (6)
20 "Amazin'" 1969 group (4)
22 Home to a prolific old woman (4)
24 It follows the overture (6)
25 One whose surname may end in -ic (4)
29 Small semicircular grooves on a column (7)
30 Persisted with (6)
32 Needing seasoning (5)
35 Words from a Styne-Cahn song (9)

Down

1 Exaggerates (4)
3 67.5 degrees, direction-wise (3)
4 Enneads (5)
5 Steak tartare, primarily (7)
6 Darin bride of 1960 (3)
8 Produce hurriedly, with "out" (5)
10 Musical setting of a text, with arias, recitatives etc (7)
11 Source of quote (10)
14 Dennis the Menace, for one (3)
16 Eats a formal meal (5)
18 Blow one's horn (4)
19 Isle of Napoleon's exile (4)
21 Operatic recitative. (5)
23 Spam producer (6)
26 Mexican-American man, for example (6)
27 Puzzlers find it bitter (5)
28 Most common of the noble gases (5)
31 Jodie Foster and Meryl Streep, collegiately (4)
33 Really move it (3)
34 __-fi (literary or film genre" (3)

CROSSWORD 32

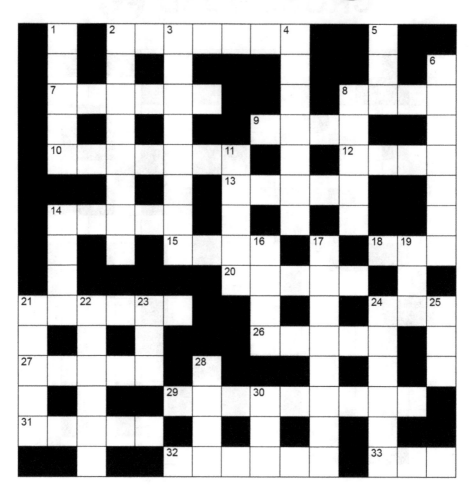

Across

2   Set-up punch (7)
7   Hall _Oates "Say It ___" (6)
8   Turn towards (4)
9   Tilted text, for short (4)
10 Like Minneapolis, vis-à-vis Miami (7)
12 Barren Alaskan island (4)
13 Stock term (5)
14 Actress Löwensohn of "Nadja" (5)
15 Airfarce's Goy (4)
18 Former flier (3)
20 "No Turn ___" (5)
21 Daily bigwig (6)
24 Noted ring leader (3)
26 Apple's music players (5)
27 Map enlargement (5)
29 Cuisinart precursor (9)
31 "__ Which Way but Loose" (5)
32 Bathroom dusting (6)
33 Training-pants wearer (3)

Down

1   Hollers (5)
2   "Alias" actress (8)
3   Cannes Film ___ (8)
4   Redeemable proofs-of-purchase, once (7)
5   ___ big (3)
6   Blotter/pencil-cup ensemble (7)
8   SOS signal (5)
11 Movie tough (5)
14 Watched carefully (4)
16 Years (4)
17 Copycat's practice (8)
19 "S" on an invitation, maybe (3)
21 Abridge (5)
22 Political debate topics (6)
23 House pooch's scrap (3)
24 Trip to the Mount Everest summit, say (6)
25 Ornamental fish (3)
28 "Adios!" (4)
30 Part of the fourth qtr. (3)

CROSSWORD 33

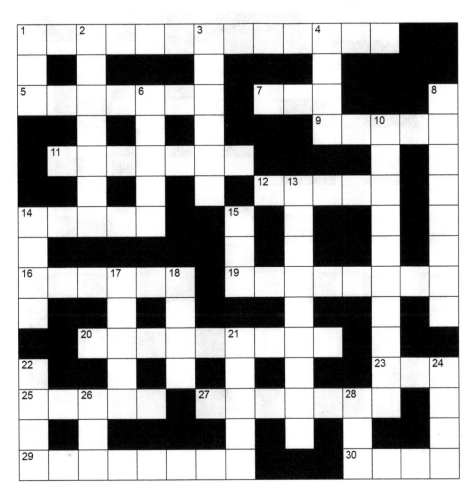

Across

1   Senior minister without portfolio, usually Leader of the House of Commons or Lords (13)
5   Trusted military chief (7)
7   "Mamma __!" (3)
9   Wavy fabric (5)
11   Marshmallow-y treat (7)
12   Choice choice of this puzzle's hidden businesses (5)
14   Large barrels (5)
16   Heavy loads (6)
19   Interference (8)
20   One who abdicates (9)
23   __ Part II (3)
25   Speed ___ (5)
27   Sounded like an angry dog (7)
29   Wholly (8)
30   Skating rink shape (4)

Down

1   Leo Durocher monicker, with "The" (3)
2   Deodorant options (7)
3   "Right?" (6)
4   Town about 10 miles from Amsterdam (4)
6   Copenhagen crowds (5)
8   Power up, as a weak battery (8)
10   Halfway to crossfaded (10)
13   Italian count's start (9)
14   Calm and controlled (4)
15   CD add-on? (3)
17   Tarot deck users (5)
18   ____-free (4)
21   Nine-person band, e.g. (5)
22   Get sore (4)
24   Doctorate seeker's hurdle (4)
26   Ship's course (3)
28   It's often subject to inflation (3)

CROSSWORD 34

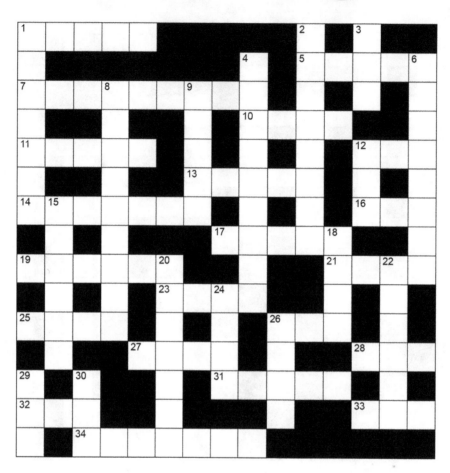

Across

1 Cotta or incognita lead-in (5)
5 Noses out (5)
7 Gag ender (9)
10 Modern Nintendo consoles (4)
11 Public ___ #1 (5)
12 Former fast plane (3)
13 Palmer, to his "army" (5)
14 Fought à la the Three Musketeers (7)
16 Word following "Hernando's hideaway" (3)
17 Tegan _Sara "One ___" (5)
19 Moved swiftly (6)
21 Peer Gynt's mother et al. (4)
23 Equally balanced (4)
25 Sounds during a massage (4)
26 Six-pack ___ (3)
27 Last ___ and testament (4)
28 Nest-egg acronym (3)
31 Drama excerpt (5)
32 Bag checking agcy. (3)
33 Juice cap in a 1990s fad (3)
34 Family outing, maybe (7)

Down

1 #1 in sports (7)
2 "Not another word!" (8)
3 Shampoo additive (3)
4 Like a recent transplant (9)
6 Moves like an anaconda (8)
8 Collector's goal (9)
9 Epic Greek tale written by Homer (5)
12 "Ray Donovan" cable channel, in TV listings (3)
15 Jazz fan, perhaps (6)
18 They perform unbelievable acts (4)
20 Great pleasure (7)
22 Potential fetus (6)
24 Fish that are found in some sushi dishes (4)
26 Trojan War god (4)
29 After-hours school group (3)
30 Deserving of a timeout (3)

CROSSWORD 35

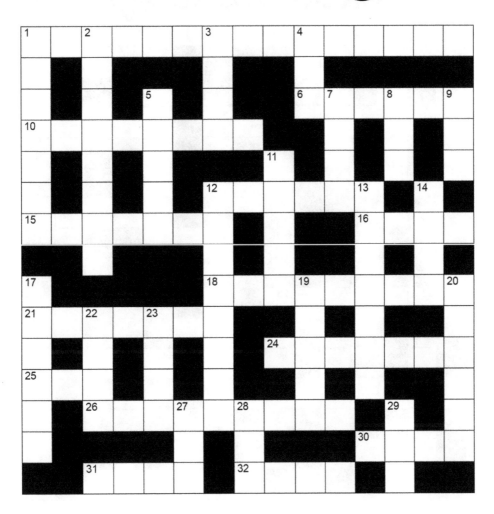

Across

1 Stiff competition (15)
6 Vacation complex (6)
10 Specified individually (8)
12 Out of business (6)
15 Sort of pass (7)
16 Potent prefix? (4)
18 September birthstones (9)
21 Unusually large or heavy (7)
24 Not done externally (7)
25 World Cup cheer (3)
26 Crustacean of rocky shores (9)
30 Asiatic lemur (4)
31 It circled Hades nine times (4)
32 Adjective on "shoppe" signs (4)

Down

1 Avant-garde (7)
2 Count noses (8)
3 Word form for "bone" (4)
4 Elton or Winston preceder (3)
5 Blake's animal (5)
7 Reese in "Legally Blonde" (4)
8 Choose (with "for") (3)
9 "The way" in Chinese philosophy (3)
11 Easy out, perhaps (5)
12 Near miss (8)
13 Half masks (7)
14 Köln closing (4)
17 Brown tea (6)
19 Columbus concern in 1492 (5)
20 Former co-host of Barbara and Joy (6)
22 Small props on a golf course (4)
23 "That ___ five minutes ago!" (4)
27 Reject (3)
28 Bezos or Buffett, e.g. (3)
29 Rank of H. Sanders (3)

CROSSWORD 36

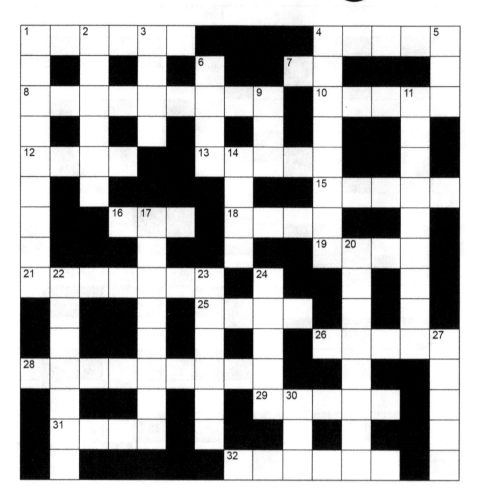

Across

1 Edit videotape, in a way (6)
4 Standards (5)
7 51 in the Forum (2)
8 Last one in, say (9)
10 Overdo, onstage (5)
12 "It should come ___ surprise" (4)
13 Score markings (5)
15 Overdo, onstage (5)
16 Place for a ring. (3)
18 Does a hen's job (4)
19 Cause for a civil action (4)
21 Israeli coins (7)
25 Tarot, e.g. (4)
26 Abolitionist-founded Kentucky college that charges no tuition (5)
28 Penn State's in it (9)
29 Eye-opener of a kind (5)
31 Need Bengay (4)
32 Reservation residence (6)

Down

1 They're barely running (9)
2 Many a telenovela watcher (6)
3 ___ the fat (chitchat) (4)
4 Most passionate (8)
5 Wiz Khalifa "___ You Again" (3)
6 Move to a different state? (4)
9 Little treasure (3)
11 It goes in the ground at a campground (9)
14 Folk singer Jenkins (4)
17 Crushed in competition (8)
20 Hand wringer's cry (8)
22 Wrapping for a Twitter user? (7)
23 Kind of whiskey (6)
24 Field of endeavor (5)
27 ___-midi (5)
30 Majors in acting (m) (3)

CROSSWORD 37

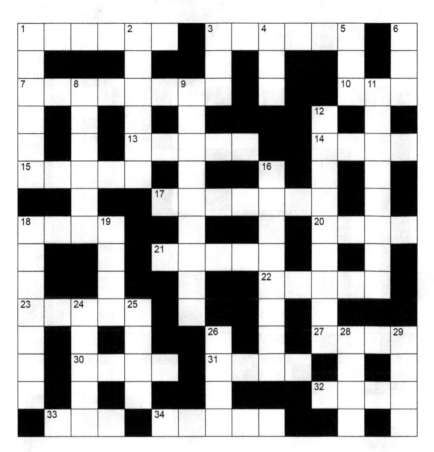

Across

1. Melissa Etheridge album featuring "Come to My Window" (6)
3. Mephitis (6)
7. Stop stewing (8)
10. Got off one's feet (3)
13. Fictional Potter (5)
14. Ornamented wig (4)
15. Former Broadway musical (5)
17. Retrieve (7)
18. Realty investment (4)
20. They adjoin the ischia (4)
21. Byelorussian capital (5)
22. Mlles., in Madrid (5)
23. Stage one may have to go through (5)
27. Train sound (4)
30. Hit song "Bette Davis ---" (4)
31. H.S. senior's exam, once (4)
32. Hershey's candy (4)
33. Quickly accelerate (3)
34. Debilitated. (5)

Down

1. Seuss title character (6)
2. Grammy-winning Franklin (6)
3. Never-___-die attitude (3)
4. Euro alliance (3)
5. They sit above nks. (3)
6. Tizzy (3)
8. Phone company ranked first in msn.com's "Customer Service Hall of Shame" (6)
9. Very conspicuous (9)
11. Blood vessels (8)
12. More than skeptical (9)
16. Two-pointer, the hard way (8)
18. Drink made of "the best stuff on earth" (7)
19. Inexpensive ASUS PCs (4)
24. Fever reducer name (5)
25. River near Kassel, Germany (4)
26. "That's it" (4)
28. Boxing blow (4)
29. Alg. follower, usually (4)

CROSSWORD 38

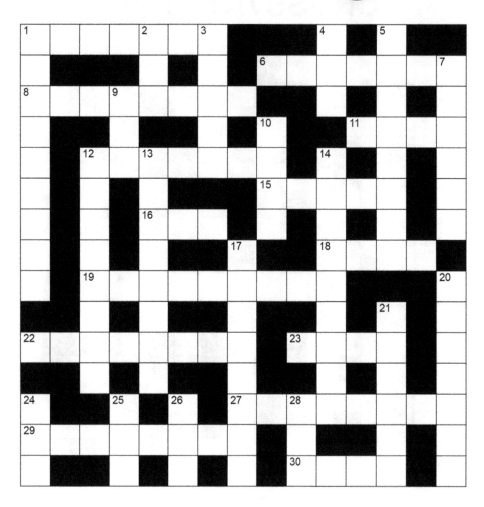

Across

1 Thalian (7)
6 They tend furnaces (7)
8 Like some statues (8)
11 __ rug (4)
12 Chaplet's kin (7)
15 Singer Mel who cowrote and sang "The Christmas Song" (5)
16 Poe's pendulum's place (3)
18 Further (4)
19 Come to an agreement, say (9)
22 Table protector (8)
23 Excellent review (4)
27 1985 Springsteen hit (8)
29 Neanderthal's time (8)
30 Egyptian goddess who was the mother of Horus (4)

Down

1 19th hole (9)
2 '-- good deed' (3)
3 Theban ruler in "Antigone" (5)
4 He hisses (3)
5 Questions after a mission (8)
7 Mason of a sort (6)
9 2011 film about a macaw named Blu (3)
10 Famous penultimate words (4)
12 Keyboard instruments (8)
13 Succeeds (8)
14 Site of Central Park concerts (9)
17 More garrulous (8)
20 Impetuous lovers (7)
21 Makes a new proposition (6)
24 Suffix after sex or fetish (3)
25 Horned grazer (3)
26 Wu-Tang Clan genre (3)
28 "... ___ will!" (3)

CROSSWORD 39

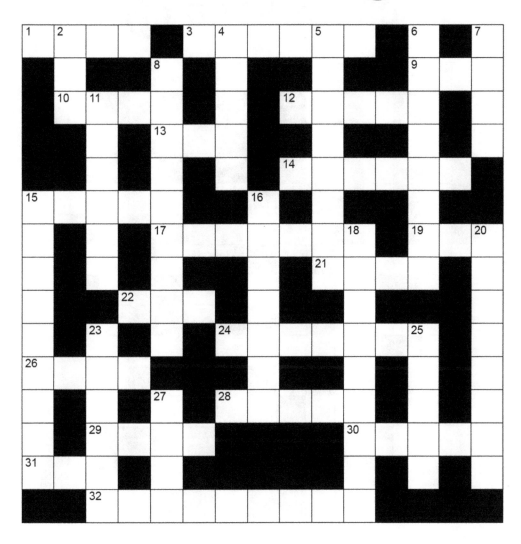

Across

1 Black, to Bernice (4)
3 Subject of a myth about night vision (6)
9 Things often dropped in Harvard Yard? (3)
10 Religious leader Roberts (4)
12 Like some baseball games (5)
13 "Give _____ rest!" (3)
14 Like the name Blake (6)
15 Beguiling tricks (5)
17 Takes to a higher court (7)
19 Without end, to poets (3)
21 Burroughs' Greystoke, for one (4)
22 Reasons for some sportscast split screens (3)
24 "Frasier" and "Fawlty Towers" (7)
26 Famous __ (4)
28 Word with "blitz" or "center" (5)
29 Do a full body scan? (4)
30 Basketful at dinner (5)
31 Discern (3)
32 Disadvantages (9)

Down

2 Cooking utensil brand (3)
4 Service station? (5)
5 "Stand by Me" actor Jerry (8)
6 Exchanged teasing remarks (8)
7 Grounded fliers (4)
8 Rapid series of notes (9)
11 Went for a spin? (6)
15 Some offensive players (9)
16 "The Cannonball Run" star (7)
18 Arias (9)
20 Driver's exam (8)
23 Sang alone (6)
25 Absolut rival, for short (5)
27 Chase on the stage (4)

CROSSWORD 40

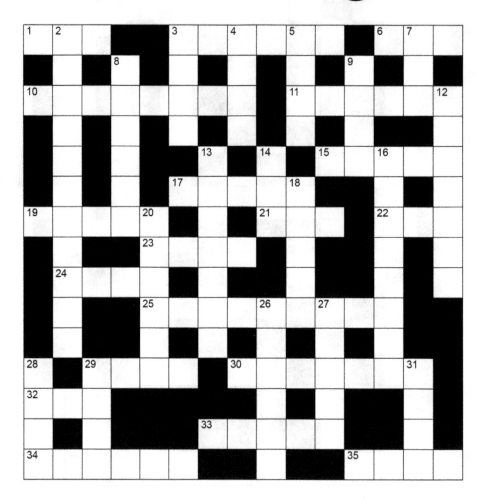

Across

1 Fort Worth campus, for short (3)
3 Entree from the frozen food department (6)
6 Truk island (3)
10 Jimmy Hoffa e.g. (8)
11 Starting point (6)
15 Marisa of "What Women Want" (5)
17 Messes with 007's martini (5)
19 Birds do it (5)
21 Vet, for one (3)
22 Bonds stat. (3)
23 Memorable quatrainist (4)
24 5000 or Vigor, e.g. (4)
25 High-powered ride (9)
29 'Downton Abbey' role (4)
30 Certain similar chemical compounds (7)
32 Fall back gradually (3)
33 Parts of a nasus (5)
34 Loft lessee, maybe (6)
35 Eurythmics "___ That Girl" (4)

Down

2 Dispel hostile feelings (11)
3 Some olive discards (4)
4 The "T" of Mr. T (4)
5 "Tiger Beat" cover subject (4)
7 Klondike discovery (3)
8 Key of 20 Haydn symphonies (6)
9 Palindromic German name (4)
12 Private teaching (7)
13 Unsatisfied worker's comment (7)
14 Certain number (3)
16 The 'who' in a whodunit (8)
18 Separates (5)
20 Kind of pen (6)
26 Nitrogen-powered devices (6)
27 Alt-rock "Wave to Make Friends" band (5)
28 Prefix for cycle (4)
29 Assist arsonists (4)
31 Orkney shed (4)

CROSSWORD 41

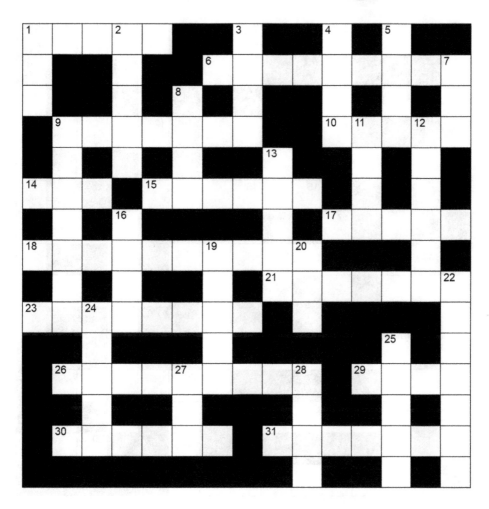

Across

1 T.R.'s "big ___" (5)
6 Make holes in, as for ease of tearing (9)
9 Effort to convince (7)
10 Marx with a fright wig (5)
14 Apparel for a Dr. Seuss cat (3)
15 Gets the job done (6)
17 City where Pixar's "Ratatouille" is set (5)
18 "Schindler's List" character (10)
21 Tender veggie (7)
23 Played on the varsity, e.g. (8)
26 Hive leaders (9)
29 Second leader (4)
30 Articulated (6)
31 Big chin-wag (7)

Down

1 Compass direction opposite NNW (3)
2 Cagney Oscar role (5)
3 Kind of bag or pole (4)
4 Nom a bit before a meal (4)
5 "The Alienist" author Caleb (4)
7 Environmentalist's favorite author? (3)
8 Stead, in legalese (4)
9 Popular quencher (7)
11 Composer-singer from Ottawa (4)
12 Polishing material (6)
13 Certain prints (5)
16 Manager's helper (4)
19 12 oz., in troy weight (5)
20 D.C.-N.Y.C. heading (3)
22 Extend, as a home (7)
24 Obama's successor (5)
25 Hall of --- (Willie Mays, e.g.) (5)
27 Ham's father, to Italians (3)
28 Lively old dance (4)

CROSSWORD 42

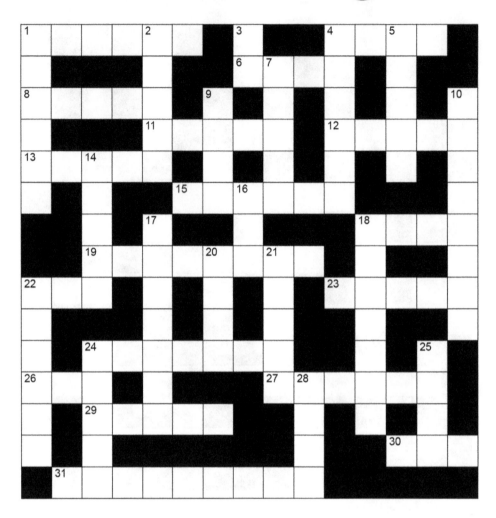

Across

1. English invader of 1066 (6)
4. Tax-form experts (4)
6. The Taj Mahal was built here (4)
8. Flops heavily, as into a beanbag chair (5)
11. Panache, e.g. (5)
12. Verdi aria "Tacea la ___ placida" (5)
13. Biblical harps (5)
15. Works a wedding, perhaps (6)
18. "Thanks, that means ___" (4)
19. Bottom line expenses (8)
22. Mer land (3)
23. The Lion, not the Witch or the Wardrobe (5)
24. Inspection chamber (7)
26. Writer Tan (3)
27. Number that's added? (6)
29. 3-line poem (5)
30. British band with "Unbelievable" (3)
31. Twinkling in the night sky (9)

Down

1. Porto italiano (6)
2. Farm animals (5)
3. Battery size (2)
4. Kim who sang "Bette Davis Eyes" (6)
5. It's ___! (5)
7. Quinks, e.g. (5)
9. Opera with chariots (4)
10. Pastime for Lucullus (8)
14. Part of Switzerland's border (5)
16. QB Detmer and others (3)
17. Tablets site (7)
18. Half-brother of Solomon (7)
20. Clued in (4)
21. Indian's castle (5)
22. Stick on the spit (6)
24. "...or I'll eat ___" (5)
25. League constituent (4)
28. Opposite of cluttered (4)

CROSSWORD 43

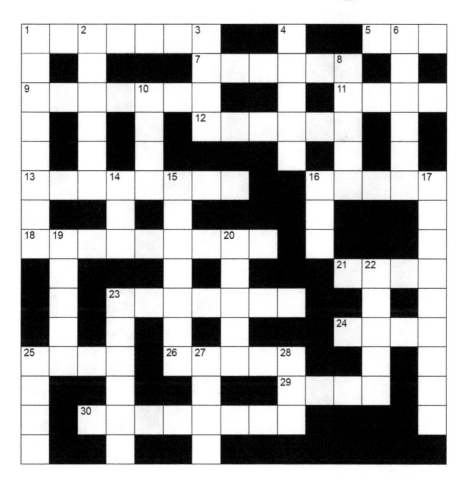

Across

1   Be a buttinsky (7)
5   "If I Ruled the World" rapper (3)
7   Lightly asleep (6)
9   Astounding (7)
11 Per item (4)
12 Gridiron play (6)
13 Person not present (8)
16 Junkyard buys (5)
18 Electrical ___ (9)
21 Refrain from swinging, to Mattingly (4)
23 Prodding to action (7)
24 Zero on Beaufort scale (4)
25 "They ___ serve . . . " (4)
26 Old blades (5)
29 Sit up and ___ notice (4)
30 Sparsely (8)

Down

1   Reagan era scandal (8)
2   Some flirts (6)
3   Outdo, barely (4)
4   Bishop's topper (5)
6   Agree to. (6)
8   Cake (5)
10 There's still some in a neodymium magnet (4)
14 "Boola Boola" singer (3)
15 Number-one (7)
16 Denali Gold Tour handout (3)
17 Like some Web videos (9)
19 British pol Farage (5)
20 Collect, as cash (5)
22 Ant that can fly (5)
23 Peanut, in the South (6)
25 Run ___ (accumulate debt at the bar) (4)
27 Typical Rick Moranis film role (4)
28 Mucky home (3)

CROSSWORD 44

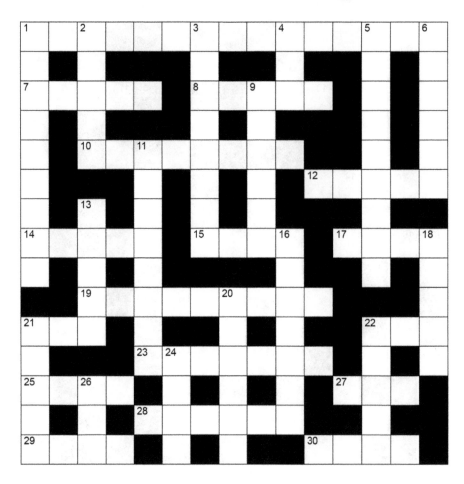

Across

1. I.O.U.'s. (15)
7. "Island of the Blue Dolphins" author Scott (5)
8. For the world to hear (5)
10. Harden (8)
12. Divided Asian country (5)
14. Indian money unit (5)
15. Long-haired dog's bane (4)
17. James who created filmdom's Charlie Allnut and Rose Sayer (4)
19. Singer with the 1980 #1 hit "Upside Down" (9)
21. Mike's candy aisle partner (3)
22. "Gym, ___, laundry" ("Jersey Shore" mantra) (3)
23. Barkeeper. (7)
25. Stretched to the max (4)
27. Sugar Loaf Mountain city (3)
28. Silent film star Normand and others (6)
29. Supplements (with "out"). (4)
30. Gig fractions (4)

Down

1. Advocates (9)
2. Droxies used to compete with them (5)
3. Impasse (8)
4. "___ are the weakest link, goodbye!" (3)
5. What 15, say, would be for leaving home (9)
6. Jon with the 1992 hit "Just Another Day" (6)
9. Springsteen "Whoa-oh-oh, I'm ___" (6)
11. Night crawlers, maybe (8)
13. Fictional sleuth (5)
16. Replies (7)
18. Wood used for piano keys (5)
20. Back from a vacation, say (6)
21. Part 2 of today's quote (5)
22. Inanimate object (5)
24. Google chat status (4)
26. "___ no hooks" (cargo-container warning) (3)

CROSSWORD 45

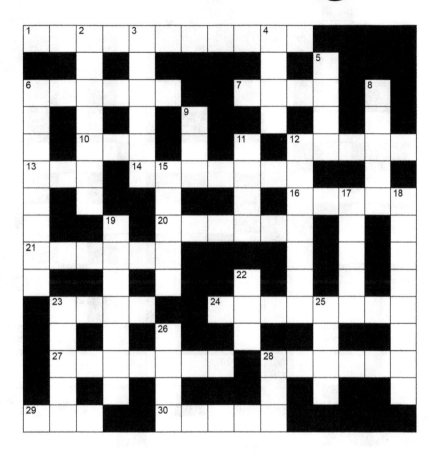

Across

1 Armistead did it at McHenry (11)
6 Ra, to some (6)
7 Be defeated (4)
10 Organization biggie, briefly (3)
12 "When dealing with people, let us remember we are not dealing with creatures of ___ " (5)
13 Pooh pal (3)
14 "You lie!" (7)
16 Switzerland city (5)
20 Holiday celebration (6)
21 Jot in the margin, say (6)
23 Canadian comedian (4)
24 NASA accomplishment (8)
27 Astray (7)
28 Bud holder (6)
29 Tie recipient, often (3)
30 Court star (5)

Down

2 Scam played out over weeks or months (7)
3 Accepted, as a job (6)
4 Elbow space (4)
5 Marlin's son in a 2003 Pixar movie (4)
6 In a top role (8)
8 Two dozen sheets (5)
9 Clubber, opposite Rocky (3)
11 "Sunday Mornin' Coming Down" singer Kristofferson (4)
12 Part of ancient Phoenicia, today (7)
15 Present for sale (5)
17 Drug agent's seizure (5)
18 Bib depictions at certain eateries (8)
19 Game with beehive-shaped pieces (7)
22 Keystone lawman (3)
23 Highest, as honors (5)
25 Spill (4)
26 Derby title? (4)
28 Art in animation books (3)

CROSSWORD 46

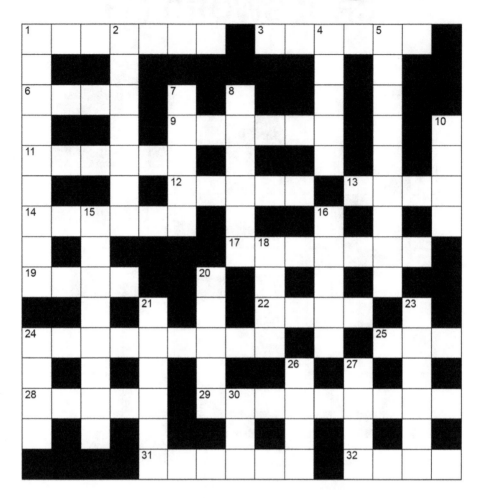

Across

1 Prepares to be eaten (7)
3 Bonzo's 1951 co-star (6)
6 ___ and board (food and lodging) (4)
9 Looker (6)
11 Backspace over, say (6)
12 Language from which "divan" is derived (5)
13 Exhausted (4)
14 "Doesn't matter to me" (6)
17 Training wheels? (7)
19 Trumped up tales (4)
22 Internet programs, in brief (4)
24 Book that's not about leprechauns (9)
25 Brand of home electronics with a dog mascot (3)
28 Al ___ (firm) (5)
29 Pressing need? (9)
31 Numerous Louvre works (6)
32 Civil War Gen. Robert ___ (4)

Down

1 Grade-school ritual (9)
2 Painting technique (7)
4 "I'm not worried" add-on (5)
5 Ticket request (9)
7 Big and muscular, as a bouncer (5)
8 Rough shredder (6)
10 Penultimate book of the Bible (4)
15 Throwing out (8)
16 Slalomer's surface (5)
18 Jake's father on "Two and a Half Men" (4)
20 Aquino's presidential successor (5)
21 Orioles, e.g., briefly (6)
23 Overture follower (6)
24 Center of the Polish film industry (4)
26 Indent settings (4)
27 City near Monaco (4)
30 Reason for overtime, in basketball (3)

CROSSWORD 47

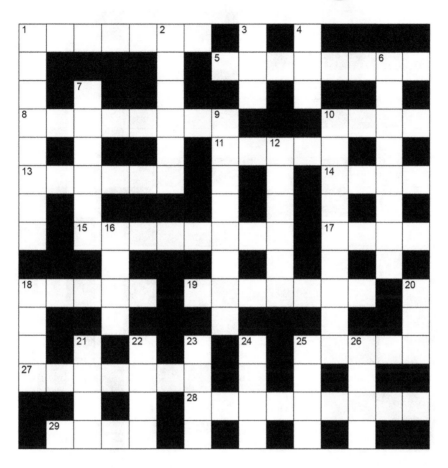

Across

1 Like a complex described by Freud (7)
5 Aristocrat (8)
8 Debbie or Ryan (8)
10 Brief biographical sketch. (4)
11 Winner's boast (5)
13 Words suggesting serious consequences (6)
14 Partner of rave (4)
15 Old coin worth two and a half new pence (8)
17 Ham operator's word (4)
18 Great or snowy, e.g. (5)
19 Phrase in a new way (7)
25 Skin, e.g. (5)
27 Feature of some bucks (7)
28 Modern way to get a virus, possibly (9)
29 New ___ (4)

Down

1 Like some food and flattery (8)
2 Prime minister between Churchill's terms (6)
3 Confusing scene (3)
4 Spa specialty, for short (3)
6 Joined the audience (8)
7 NL East squad (6)
9 Suppressor of a report (8)
10 Montpelier resident (9)
12 Uneasy state (6)
16 'The -- of March' (2011 film) (4)
18 Scandinavian collection that influenced Tolkien (4)
20 Governor at Topeka. (3)
21 Dip __ in (4)
22 Only a stone's throw away (4)
23 Teacher's graduate deg. (4)
24 Total guess (4)
25 Old masters used them (4)
26 Some baby-talk words (4)

CROSSWORD 48

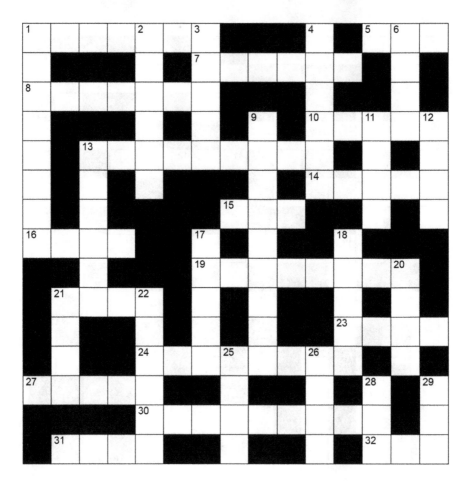

Across

1   James Mattis was one (7)
5   Alfred E. Neuman's magazine (3)
7   Advertiser's order (6)
8   Went on the blink (7)
10 Emcee's task, often (5)
13 Annual black-tie broadcast, familiarly (9)
14 Spartan serf (5)
15 Elevenses in London (3)
16 Reason for a timeout, perhaps (4)
19 Rural (8)
21 Where Furka Pass is. (4)
23 End (4)
24 Stressful spots (8)
27 Yogi who misspeaks (5)
30 Undeveloped ability (9)
31 Prefix meaning '10' (4)
32 Road coverage (3)

Down

1   Endowed individuals (8)
2   Declaration signer from Delaware (6)
3   Northern people (5)
4   Touch up, like a candidate for office? (6)
6   Middle-___ (person who's fiftyish) (4)
9   Circular figure? (9)
11 Fuentes (4)
12 Like some fried food (4)
13 Glittery tree decoration (6)
17 Soul seller of legend (5)
18 Guru followers (5)
20 River past Memphis (4)
21 Lima lung filler (4)
22 Large hot spot (6)
25 "The sun never ___ on the British Empire" (4)
26 Sycamore, e.g. (4)
28 Legal pers. (3)
29 Prior's always (3)

CROSSWORD 49

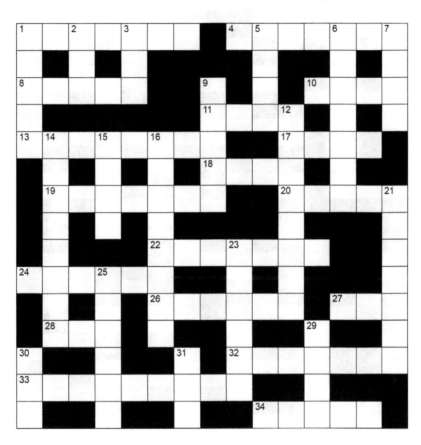

Across

1 Way better than average (7)
4 Builds up (7)
8 "Let's make some ___!" (5)
10 Medicinal lily (4)
11 Org. of which Venezuela is a member (4)
13 Ill-fated U.S. submarine of 1968 (8)
17 "This ___ a Love Song" Bon Jovi (4)
18 Fourth of a pint (4)
19 Lynx lynx, e.g. (7)
20 Bankers' protections (5)
22 By then (7)
24 Famous frog (6)
26 Like the hardest bread (6)
27 Indy service center (3)
28 Grizzled sailor (3)
32 About to be a mom (7)
33 Maims (9)
34 Composer Barraine and others (5)

Down

1 Lady ___, Girl Guides founder (5)
2 "Rumble in the Jungle" fighter (3)
3 "___ got a golden ticket" (lyric sung by Grandpa Joe) (3)
5 Puzzle with passages (4)
6 Taciturnity (7)
7 Move for O'Connor or Kelly (4)
9 Salad-serving implements (5)
12 Guessed right (8)
14 Victorian home feature (8)
15 Pondside stalk (4)
16 Copier (8)
21 Barack Obama was one (7)
23 Tropical resins (6)
25 1990's Fox sitcom (6)
29 Some stingers (4)
30 "It's Dark and Hell is Hot" rapper (3)
31 There are two to a qt. (3)

CROSSWORD 50

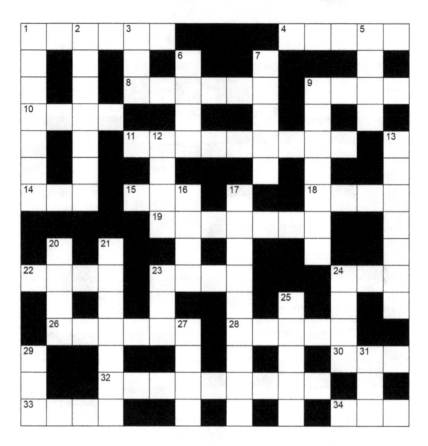

Across

1 Fly ___ mushroom (6)
4 "Midnight Cowboy" nickname (5)
8 The big house? (6)
9 Fuse together with a blowtorch (4)
10 Disc-shaped sweet (4)
11 Waterfront worker (9)
14 Mork and Alf (3)
15 Latin 'I love' (3)
18 Collar straightener (4)
19 Alan Paton, e.g. (7)
22 Man-goat deity (4)
23 Wolf of the West (4)
24 What a Tennessee cheerleader asks for a lot? (3)
26 "Jeopardy!" staple (6)
28 Mathematical proportion (5)
30 Dir. opposite to WbS (3)
32 Leader exiled on Saint Helena (9)
33 Movable shelter (4)
34 Savings accts. (3)

Down

1 Set free from guilt (7)
2 States unequivocally (7)
3 "___ not a tumor!" (classic rebuke in "Kindergarten Cop") (3)
5 Window rest (4)
6 "Going ___, going..." (4)
7 Even bet (5)
9 Alternative to a ticket (7)
12 Like "Nip/Tuck," rating-wise (4)
13 Obscurities (7)
16 Point __ return (4)
17 Actress Weaver of "Alien" (9)
20 Tout à ___ (entirely, in French) (4)
21 Time-honored (7)
23 Festive neckwear (3)
24 ___ water (trendy drink) (4)
25 The _____ Angel, by M. Laurence (5)
27 Like, so much (4)
29 Termite (3)
31 Terse reprimand (3)

CROSSWORD 51

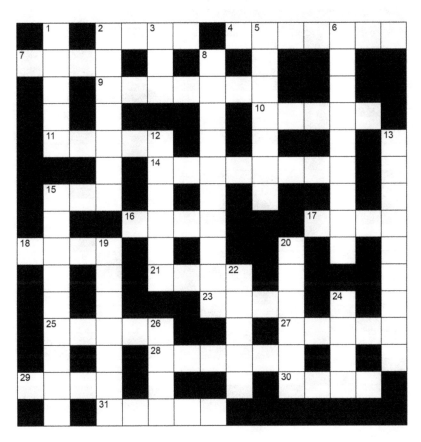

Across

2 CBS spin-off of "JAG" (4)
4 A bit like custard or mustard? (7)
7 Execute again (4)
9 Skater's leap (7)
10 Less youthful (5)
11 Rod-shaped bacteria (5)
14 Paintings often including an infant (8)
15 Leader of Denmark? (3)
16 Diarist's sheet (4)
17 Fairy (4)
18 Word sung twice after "que" (4)
21 Add to or remove from (4)
23 Arena (4)
25 Its border with Canada is less than fifty miles long (5)
27 Have effect (5)
28 Berry Gordy's hit factory (6)
29 Locale of "plenty of seats" (4)
30 Country rock's Parsons (4)
31 Noted jazz bandleader (5)

Down

1 Ninnies (5)
2 Unfinished (7)
3 "___ Road Truckers" (History Channel show) (3)
5 Ireland's currency unit since 2001 (7)
6 Proprietor's status (9)
8 Billy Graham had his own pavilion there in 1964 (10)
12 "What a loooong day!" (6)
13 Disney classic starring Spike the dog (9)
15 Junks (9)
19 News _current ... (7)
20 Wild (6)
22 Lesser (5)
24 Hawaii ... grass skirts ... Bowl (4)
26 "The ___"(2006 remake of a horror film about an evil boy named Damien) (4)

CROSSWORD 52

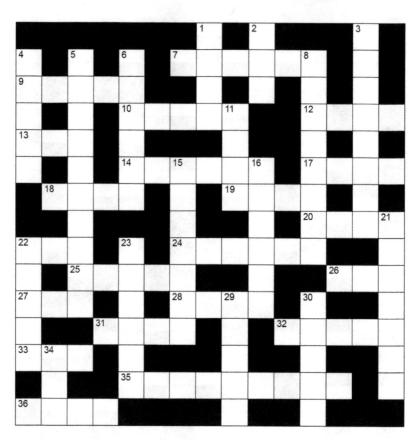

Across

7 Tied up, as a ship (6)
9 Bagel or yogurt choice (5)
10 Deck with the Fool and the World (5)
12 "Giralda" composer (4)
13 ". . . ___ gloom of night" (3)
14 Shade trees (6)
17 "Heaven make thee free ___!" (4)
18 Lawn problem (4)
19 Nation without political parties (4)
20 Cope with (4)
22 Govt. product-tester (3)
24 Some beets (6)
25 Governor before Pataki (5)
26 Dye type (3)
27 "Rocky III" star (3)
28 Tough times (4)
31 Vegas numbers game (4)
32 Student of France (5)
33 Deplorable. (3)
35 Santana song (9)
36 Lacking moisture (4)

Down

1 Only OK (4)
2 Star, e.g. (3)
3 Only winner of six straight European Figure Skating titles besides Sonja (8)
4 Side of a book (5)
5 Legislation of 2001 (10)
6 Wild (6)
8 Tigers' habitats (8)
11 Vincent's lifelong ally (4)
15 Flutelike instrument (7)
16 Round-the-campfire treats (6)
21 Most flexible (7)
22 Unpleasant vapour (5)
23 Corrida star (6)
29 Heiress, perhaps (5)
30 Naproxen trade name (5)
34 Ginger chaser (3)

CROSSWORD 53

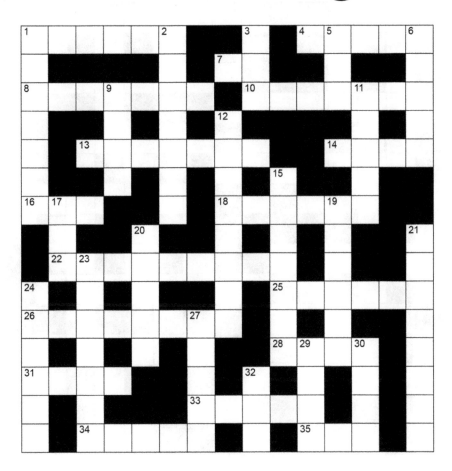

Across

1   Certain New York team (6)
4   She played Connie in "The Godfather" (5)
7   Turin's river (2)
8   ___ Joan Hart of TV's "Sabrina" (7)
10 Businessman's attire (7)
13 .45 or .22 (7)
14 Works at (4)
16 Wally's exclamation (3)
18 Taipei's island (6)
22 Cather novel set in Nebraska (9)
25 Former Disney CEO Michael (6)
26 Reported by phone (8)
28 Purport (4)
31 Husband, in France (4)
33 Run off to marry (5)
34 "... and the truth ___ set you free" (5)
35 "Gee!" (3)

Down

1   Kill holder (7)
2   With freshness (7)
3   Cubs Hall of Famer Santo (3)
5   Commandments bearer (3)
6   Specializations (5)
9   Big-screen format that "Dunkirk" was filmed in (4)
11 "Achilles and the Tortoise" subject Mark (5)
12 Make oneself comfortable (8)
15 Aromatic root (7)
17 Super add-on (3)
19 Brings low (6)
20 Band of 13 witches (5)
21 Plumb (8)
23 U.S.N. missile (7)
24 Kitchen visitors of yore (6)
27 Chip shipper (5)
29 Agenda subject (4)
30 Saturday AM TV star (4)
32 Decompose naturally (3)

CROSSWORD 54

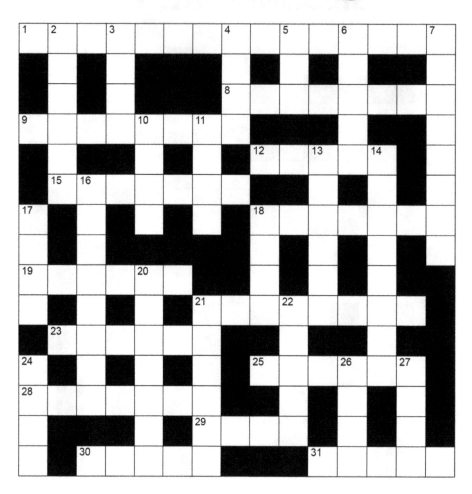

Across

1 1929 novel, and this puzzle's title (15)
8 Depicted (8)
9 Ornamental shrub with rose-like flowers (8)
12 "Me too!" relative (5)
15 Fifth, e.g. (7)
18 Chinese e-commerce conglomerate (7)
19 Racetrack equipment (6)
21 One drawing many blanks (8)
23 Capital of ancient Lydia (6)
25 Most mature (6)
28 "I should hit the hay" (7)
29 Burn quickly (4)
30 Browsing history entries (5)
31 Cry on a battlefield (5)

Down

2 Mozart's "Le Nozze di ___" (6)
3 ___ Aid (4)
4 Small constellation (4)
5 Weigh station unit, perhaps (3)
6 Best athletes (5)
7 Of the stars (8)
10 Revealed, with "open" (4)
11 "--- See for Miles" (4)
13 Clapton "Journeyman" rocker "No ___" (6)
14 Residents of Canyon County (8)
16 Steaks and chops (8)
17 Fast-flying planes (4)
18 "Got two fives for ___?" (4)
20 Made a new hand (7)
21 Place a value on (6)
22 One who sniggles (5)
24 "___ Don't Lie" (#1 hit for Shakira) (4)
26 "___ Kleine Nachtmusik" (4)
27 Garr of the screen (4)

CROSSWORD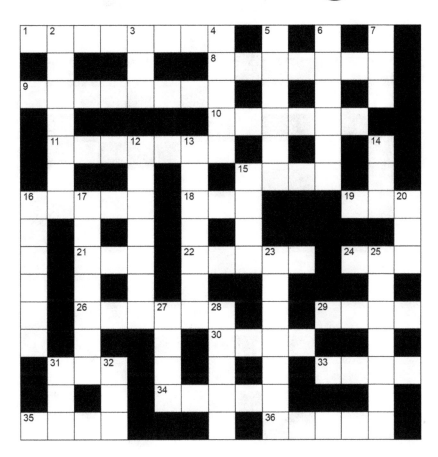

Across

1 Leo Durocher's losers (8)
8 Like an old schoolhouse (7)
9 Flute relative (8)
10 Amazon's home (6)
11 Lottery with a rotating drum (7)
15 Conclaves (4)
16 Hammerstein creation (5)
18 Greek goddess of punishment (3)
19 Abe Vigoda's role in "The Godfather" (3)
21 Lisa Simpson's paternal grandfather (3)
22 Sandbox retort (5)
24 Storm heading (3)
26 Mollusk often served marinara (6)
29 Ace for one (4)
30 Fashion magazine begun in France (4)
31 Photo possibilities (3)
33 Turbulent currents (4)
34 Strawberry, once, briefly (5)
35 Team moving to Brooklyn in 2012 (4)
36 Like faulty beer taps (5)

Down

2 Without motion (7)
3 Sound that means "Back off!" (3)
4 Kind of, informally (5)
5 Move at a restaurant, say (6)
6 Powered bicycles (6)
7 GPs' gp. (3)
12 Angels on Broadway (7)
13 Result of bad insulation (7)
14 Org. with millions of members HQ'd in Fairfax, Va. (3)
15 Athletic contest (4)
16 Certain protests (6)
17 AAA handout (7)
20 Near the ground (3)
23 Fluffy fare (7)
25 Feisty (7)
27 Work on the web (4)
28 Proposition for proving a theorem (5)
31 Framed bill in a restaurant, perhaps (3)
32 Sound from a leaking tire (3)

CROSSWORD 56

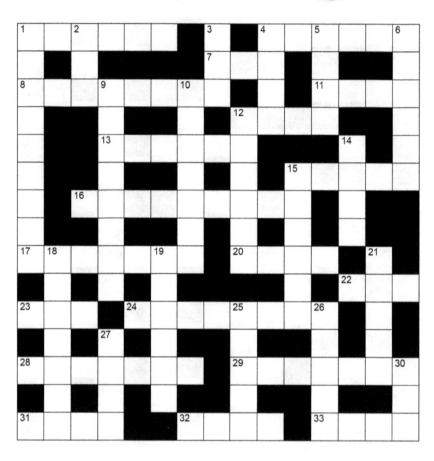

Across

1 Cottonwood, for one (6)
4 Particles (6)
7 Greeting for Gaius (3)
8 Lily's Ernestine, e.g. (8)
11 Cat, in Córdoba (4)
12 Workplace regulator (4)
13 Large dog (6)
15 Dartmouth, Yale, etc. (5)
16 Something torn out from a catalog (9)
17 Speaks for (7)
20 Garden ornaments (4)
22 Scarce physicians (3)
23 In the past. (3)
24 Not let go of (8)
28 Reference book compiler, at times (7)
29 More palatable (7)
31 1970s-'80s sitcom setting (4)
32 "___ Reader" ("A Different Read on Life" magazine) (4)
33 Jack and Jill, e.g. (4)

Down

1 Work on galleys (9)
2 Edgar Allan who quothed the Raven "nevermore" (3)
3 Cause of stubborn stains (3)
4 Imagines (4)
5 Tune from Shankar (4)
6 Bends down (6)
9 Overseas vet who's come home (8)
10 In some ways (7)
12 Goldlike brass (6)
14 ___ of Worms (4)
15 'Right away, boss!' (6)
18 Wife of Louis Napoleon (7)
19 Crown (6)
21 Jobs can be found there (5)
25 "Vote early, vote ___" (5)
26 In-a-bottle alternative (5)
27 Parts of mins. (4)
30 Capek play (3)

CROSSWORD 57

Across

1 Gandhi's birthday, a holiday in India (15)
5 Tap anew (6)
8 The Grateful ___ (4)
10 God depicted holding a crook (6)
12 Some Crown Royal offerings (4)
13 Drive dangerously, in a way (8)
15 Cop show with the line "Just the facts, ma'am" (7)
16 Currently (6)
18 Chorus members (6)
19 Potential pipe (3)
20 Cardiology graphs, for short (4)
22 Race winner of fable (8)
26 Suit worn with a cummerbund, for short (3)
27 Sedan named for an Italian city (5)
28 Goodman specialty (5)
29 Word with "zinc" or "nitrous" (5)
30 "I gotta run!" (5)

Down

1 Text of a film (6)
2 Plains tribesman (4)
3 Bakery buy (9)
4 Early date finisher (3)
6 Certain diets (6)
7 Produced (5)
9 Optical openings (9)
11 Go into a skid (5)
12 Spoke endlessly (5)
14 Invasion (6)
17 Tidal return (3)
20 Inflated ones often clash (4)
21 Tin (5)
22 Hippolyte of France (5)
23 Baseball's Martinez (4)
24 Land where Moguls once reigned (5)
25 Word on Irish currency (4)

CROSSWORD 58

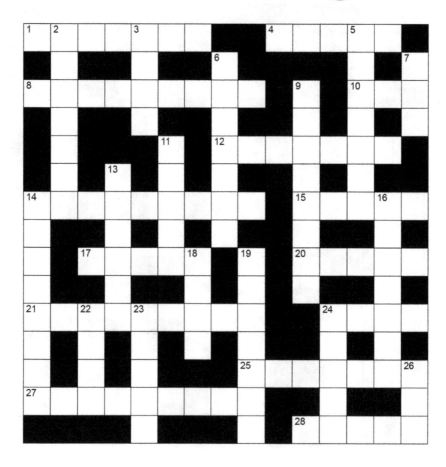

Across

1   Reason to get dolled up (7)
4   Sourdough's deed (5)
8   Time to come (9)
10   Schumer's title (3)
12   Devices for clearing winter sidewalks (7)
14   New York's sugar maple, e.g. (9)
15   "___ Tear Fall in the River" (5)
17   Skirt named for a letter (5)
20   "Look for yourself" (5)
21   Traveling bag (9)
24   Calculator display components, for short (4)
25   Milk sources nowadays (7)
27   Fries, maybe (9)
28   Have children, old-style (5)

Down

2   It isn't repeated (7)
3   First on the scene? (4)
5   "Insecure" star (7)
6   Pascal work (7)
7   "Star Wars" saga nickname (3)
9   Gypsy cloths (8)
11   What most college mottoes are in (5)
13   Lost zip (6)
14   Viral disease causing severe neuralgia (8)
16   Continued in one direction, like the stock market (7)
18   Teamwork wreckers (4)
19   Of food intake (7)
22   Like much of New Mexico (4)
23   Route for a bloodhound (5)
24   Africa's Sierra ___ (5)
26   All prepared (3)

CROSSWORD 59

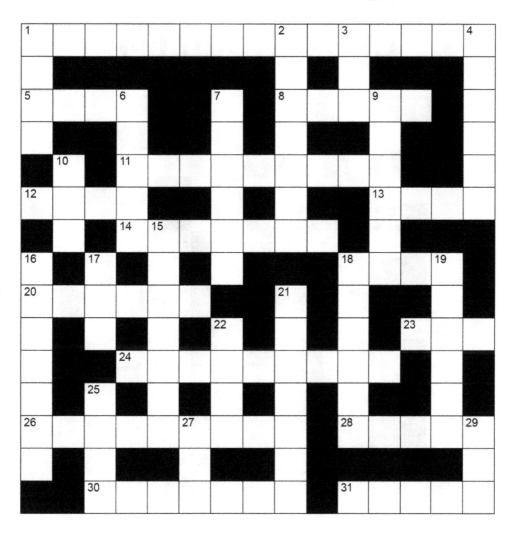

Across

1. End of the question (15)
5. Banister (4)
8. Courtroom drama with Susan Dey (5)
11. Ill temper (9)
12. Fist name in the "Titanic" cast (4)
13. Diminishes gradually (4)
14. Antenna housings on aircraft (7)
18. Editor's "my bad" (4)
20. "Spare me!" (6)
23. Lead-in to X, Y or Z (3)
24. There are 15 to a rack (9)
26. Cut (9)
28. "Zoo Story" playwright (5)
30. Pounded with a pestle (7)
31. Consumes less (5)

Down

1. Off the beaten track (4)
2. Fitness whiz Jack (7)
3. Small particle (abbr.) (3)
4. Beach garb (6)
6. He doesn't like company (5)
7. Six feet down? (6)
9. The A of AWOL (6)
10. Downward bend (3)
15. Breathing tube part (7)
16. Gumshoe (7)
17. Band box? (3)
18. Antonin of the Supreme Court (6)
19. Feared fly (6)
21. Like a venetian blind (7)
22. Voice from a loft (4)
25. Title for a pageant winner? (4)
27. Doggy treater (abbr.) (3)
29. Chicago bearers? (3)

CROSSWORD 60

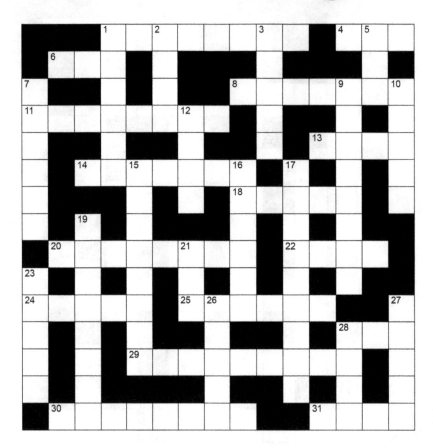

Across

1 Earring shape, often (8)
4 Ecclesiastical deg. (3)
6 "Sure thing" (3)
8 Babylonian's rival (7)
11 Author Uris's nickname when he was in the "Round and Round" rock group? (8)
13 Bank guard? (4)
14 First — beginning (7)
18 Dog show entrant (5)
20 Assumed to be true (8)
22 Joint (4)
24 Cowboy show (5)
25 Tomorrow in Barcelona (6)
28 Int'l carrier in "The Aviator" (3)
29 Surgical removals (9)
30 Relief provider (8)
31 Calls upon (4)

Down

1 "Room at ___" (6)
2 Downwind at sea (4)
3 Cause of rust (5)
5 It's passed for money (3)
7 Sea anchor (6)
9 Simulated (8)
10 Biz bigwigs (5)
12 Shock jock Gregg Hughes, on XM Radio (4)
15 Headset (8)
16 Where dirty work is done? (6)
17 Poetic Emily (9)
19 Butch's pal (8)
21 Mendes who's slated to direct the next James Bond film (3)
23 French side? (5)
26 April 1 child, e.g. (5)
27 Vacation home spots (5)
28 Menu possessive linked to the Qing dynasty (4)

CROSSWORD 61

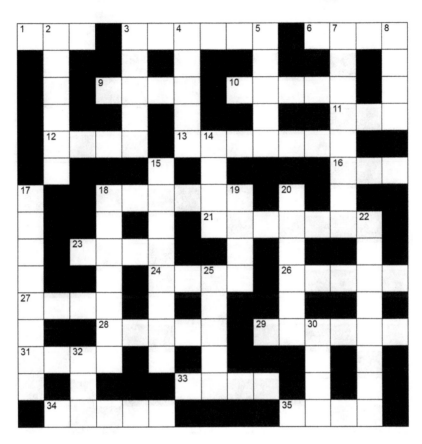

Across

1   Mil. landing craft (3)
3   Large number (6)
6   "I get it now" (4)
9   Freeman Gosden (4)
10 Model-airplane assembler, often (5)
11 Use Manic Panic, e.g. (3)
12 Modern cheesecake ingredient (4)
13 Grabs some shuteye (7)
16 "I Love You, ___" (2009 Paul Rudd comedy) (3)
18 Certain tics (6)
21 Site for some celebratory dances (7)
23 Military sch. (4)
24 Glean (4)
26 Water lifter (5)
27 Puny parasite (4)
28 1953 film gunslinger (5)
29 San Diego County's San --- (6)
31 Sp. married women (4)
33 Garden Guns was "lost" in (4)
34 Torah expert (5)
35 Beautify (4)

Down

2   Yiddish author Aleichem (6)
3   Fast Cuban dance (5)
4   Sets' opposite (5)
5   Big name in car batteries (5)
7   Keeper of sheep (8)
8   Single occurrence (4)
14 Where the Iditarod dogsled race ends, after beginning in Anchorage (4)
15 Nightmare (8)
17 Custardy dessert (8)
18 Opposite of failure (7)
19 Trim with scissors (4)
20 Web mags (6)
22 Where to get off (8)
25 To come (5)
30 Gregg Allman "___ Angel" (4)
32 Dudley the Dinosaur's org. (3)

CROSSWORD 62

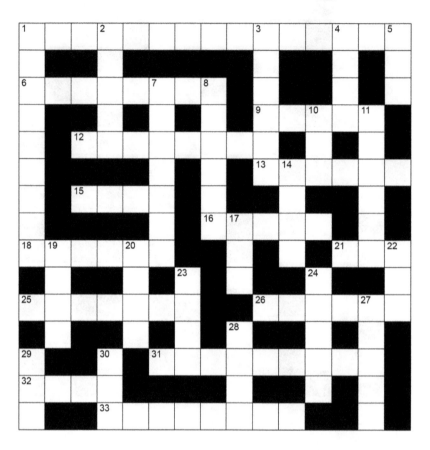

Across

1 Flowers-of-an-hour (15)
6 Legal docket (8)
9 Home for Jacques Chirac (5)
12 Lease co-signer (8)
13 Where one might be held up (6)
15 Scopes of the Scopes Monkey Trial (4)
16 Regal accessory (5)
18 Home to the Venus de Milo (6)
21 Org. for the Williams sisters (3)
25 Where Starbucks' started (7)
26 Concerns of sprinters (6)
31 It's named for the Sun King (9)
32 Glass rectangle (4)
33 Bias (8)

Down

1 Retreat (9)
2 Motto (5)
3 Middle ear bone (6)
4 Part of the Constitution that describes Cong. powers (4)
5 35mm camera option (3)
7 Considerable (7)
8 Cause of the 1773 "party" (6)
10 Feel badly about (3)
11 Lose one's patience with, maybe (6)
14 One of three brothers in the Old West (4)
17 Hairiest cousin imaginable (3)
19 Kind of mitt (4)
20 Dirt road sights (4)
22 Pro- -- (some tourneys) (3)
23 Fiddler or pianist (4)
24 Six-Day War hero (5)
27 Bygone Russian rulers (5)
28 Display board. (4)
29 PDA download (3)
30 Get spliced (3)

CROSSWORD 63

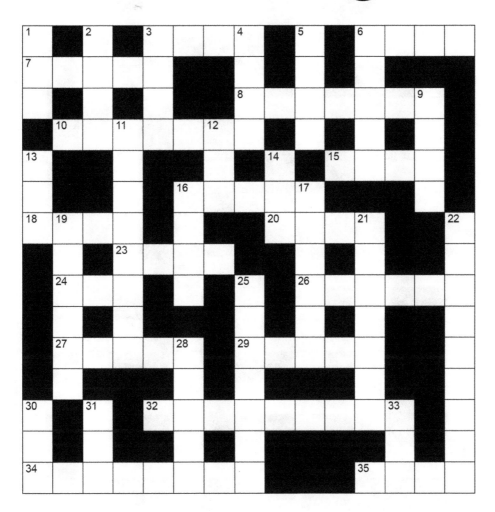

Across

3   Elvis' daughter ___ Marie (4)
6   Linebacker Junior who debuted in 1990 and still hasn't retired (4)
7   "___ the World" (1985 song that raised over $60 million for charity) (5)
8   "Lili ___," 1944 song (7)
10 Steinbeck's poodle (7)
15 It's a lot less slimy if you roast it, actually (4)
16 Get ___ start (5)
18 Word accompanied by a gavel rap (4)
20 Gives the gate to (4)
23 React to a shock like an angler? (4)
24 Mother of Eos and Selene (3)
26 Really angry (6)
27 Cleaves. (5)
29 "I'd have to __ to ..." (5)
32 Join the cast? (9)
34 Some Bach pieces (8)
35 Letter after epsilon (4)

Down

1   Bankrupt airline (3)
2   Multiplying, e.g. (4)
3   Annealing oven (4)
4   Group of companies (4)
5   AOL or IBM, e.g. (4)
6   ___ attack (5)
9   "Holy moly!" (4)
11 Harmful downfall (8)
12 Japanese food fish (3)
13 "Say what?" sounds (3)
14 __ glance (3)
16 Becomes less green (4)
17 Sin tax, e.g. (6)
19 Bewhiskered mammals (6)
21 Helter-___ (7)
22 Eleanor H. Porter work (9)
25 Scott Pelley's workplace (7)
28 Quick pass in football (5)
30 ___ Garfunkel (3)
31 Pitcher Dwight Gooden's nickname (3)
33 You might slice from it (3)

CROSSWORD 64

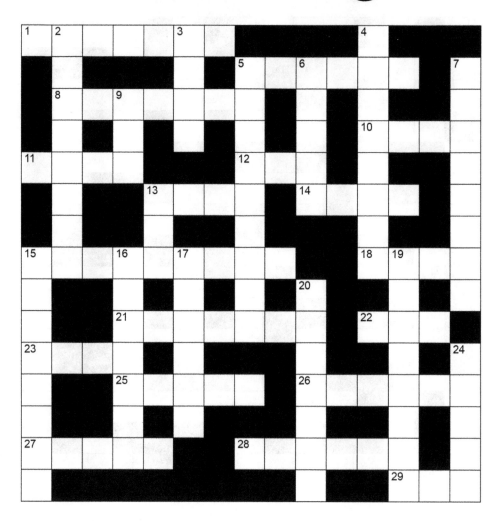

Across

1 Runaway (7)
5 Child actress? (6)
8 Very convenient, as shopping (7)
10 Job application data (4)
11 Chide, with "off" (4)
12 Sock tip (3)
13 Menu choice for the fallible (4)
14 Greek letters (4)
15 Lighting specialists? (9)
18 Israeli port (4)
21 Fall forecast phrase (7)
22 ___-Cat (winter off-road vehicle) (3)
23 Brand with "Did you pivot today?" ads (4)
25 Squished square (5)
26 Tintoretto's "The Miracle of ___ Freeing the Slave" (6)
27 Controversial explosion (5)
28 Not at all chubby (6)
29 "Now it's like 'Murder, ___ Wrote' once I get you out them clothes" (R. Kelly lyric) (3)

Down

2 Perfumery purchase (8)
3 "Tell __ the Marines" (4)
4 Strand (8)
5 Just a little cupful, in Britain (9)
6 More auspicious (5)
7 Pricey car with a trident emblem (8)
9 Member of a certain order (3)
13 Vase relative (3)
15 Pen called "The Rock" (8)
16 Bovine-pulled vehicles (7)
17 Noted 1950 short story collection (6)
19 Genealogists' pursuits (8)
20 Fire basket (7)
24 Emulate Apolo Ohno (5)

CROSSWORD 65

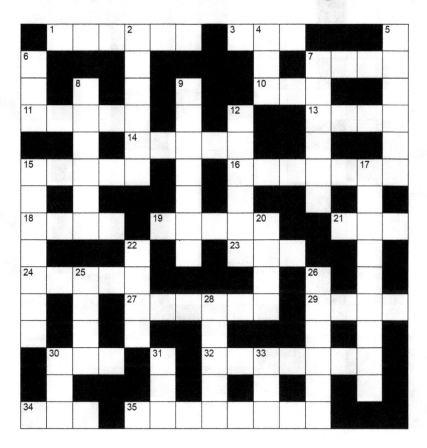

Across

1 Without reciprocity (6)
3 LAX overseer (3)
7 Heroic tale (4)
10 Work in a studio (3)
11 Fabric favored at Colonial Williamsburg (5)
13 Elec. current initials (4)
14 Lamb Chop's instructor (5)
15 Military supply station (5)
16 Backscratch, politically (7)
18 Brushoffs (4)
19 Part of the plumbing (5)
21 It adds some kick to Coke (3)
23 Of oneself (3)
24 Bowie's nemesis (5)
27 Currency container (6)
29 American revolutionary buried at the Kremlin (4)
30 Eisenhower's military rank (3)
32 Back strokes? (7)
34 Sticky icky stuff (3)
35 Best of the best, sportswise (8)

Down

2 Having the most space (6)
4 Caribbean music genre of "Mirror in the Bathroom" band The English Beat (3)
5 Little bugger (6)
6 Not a good thing to go to (3)
7 Indoor flight (6)
8 WW2 Battlefield (6)
9 Ornate writing (7)
12 Country singer with a noteworthy stutter (6)
15 "Next subject, please" (7)
17 Washed (clothes) (9)
20 "Café de ___" (Van Gogh) (4)
22 Meteorologists' depressions (4)
25 Prior (to) (4)
26 Some candies (6)
28 Some green garnishes (5)
30 Sloppy stuff (3)
31 Soviet chess-master (3)
33 Hot spot (3)

CROSSWORD 66

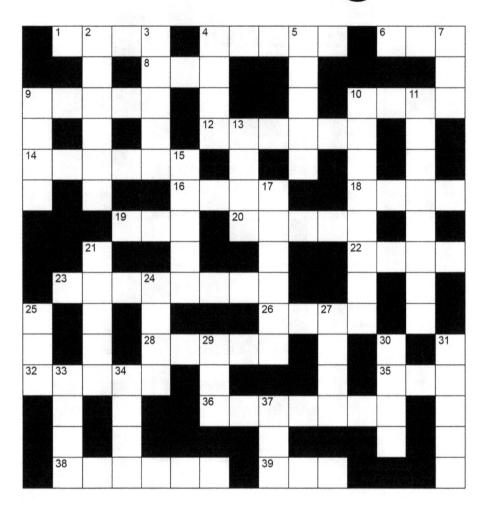

Across

1 Taiwan-based computer maker (4)
4 Latin girlfriend (5)
6 White House monogram (3)
8 Twin with a connection (3)
9 Some businesswear (5)
10 Cuisine for corporals (4)
12 Severe chest problem (6)
14 Lennon's last home, with 'The' (6)
16 Okefenokee growth (4)
18 Like Monday crosswords, relatively speaking (4)
19 Goal of some start-ups (3)
20 SL customers (5)
22 Prefix with play or scope (4)
23 Wheeled symbol of San Francisco (8)
26 Engr.'s specialty (4)
28 "I've got half ___ to ..." (5)
32 Pen pal? (5)
35 Batman and Robin are a dynamic one (3)
36 Asahi competitor (7)
38 By-passer of large wedding. (6)
39 Quote from a goat (3)

Down

2 Brings up a menu with a PC mouse (6)
3 Convene anew (5)
4 Golfo de México contents (4)
5 Comedian Rock (5)
7 They get firmer when crunched (3)
9 Fizz in a gin fizz (4)
10 Regal (8)
11 Briny residue (8)
13 US agency featured in "The Martian" (4)
15 Signorina's love (5)
17 Goose-pimply (6)
21 Sports coat feature (5)
24 7-time Oscar best director nominee (4)
25 Santa's helper at the North Pole (3)
27 Hollow reply? (4)
29 They take W-2s (3)
30 Gardenia or lilac (4)
31 Sea or snake (5)
33 One-named model (4)
34 Mingle-mangle (4)
37 Title character in a Poe novel (3)

CROSSWORD 67

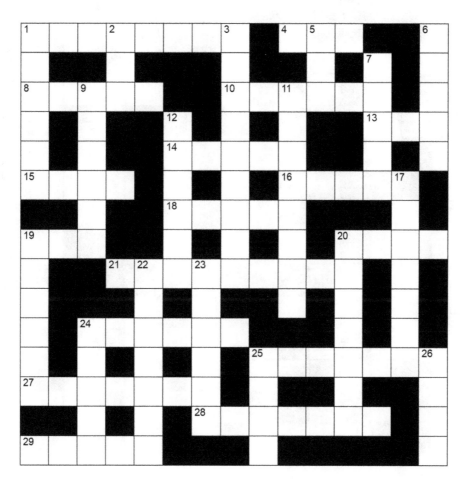

Across

1 Mark (8)
4 Melding card (3)
8 Eyes roguishly (5)
10 Roof type for many (6)
13 Sno-cone base (3)
14 Mongoose foe (5)
15 High-five, for one (4)
16 Less coarse (5)
18 Still in draft form (5)
19 Biblical prophet (3)
20 Like Marlee Matlin (4)
21 1961 Pulitzer-winning novelist (9)
24 Italian opera venue (6)
25 Controlled (7)
27 Globe, e.g. (7)
28 Some engraving tools (7)
29 More pink, as steak (5)

Down

1 Oak nuts (6)
2 Number of F's in this puzzle's answer grid (3)
3 Famous last words (9)
5 Mehitabel, for one (3)
6 Weight-loss ad caption word (5)
7 ___ Valley, German wine region (5)
9 ["I'm not listening!"] (6)
11 Jr. of "Gilligan's Island" (8)
12 One crossing the plate (6)
17 Colts' former home (7)
19 None the worse for wear (6)
20 Boldly resistant — fainted (anag) (7)
22 Connection gizmo (7)
23 Picks apart a sentence (6)
24 It's human, so it is said (5)
25 It may be held at a diner (4)
26 Tragic (4)

CROSSWORD 68

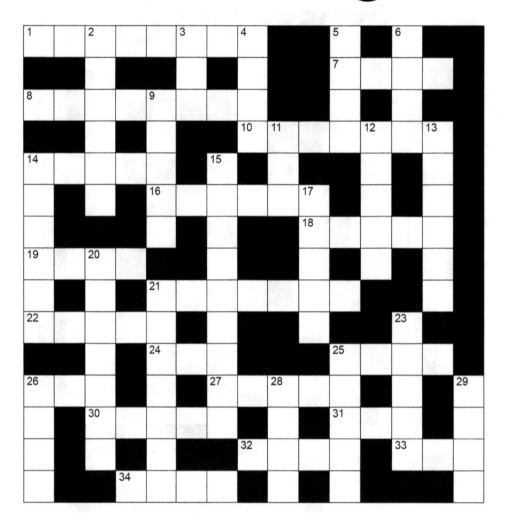

Across

1   Make a remix for YouTube, often (8)
7   Skin care additive (4)
8   Restaurant offering that might come with a toy (8)
10 Dirge (7)
14 Featherweight champion of the world, e.g. (5)
16 Macduff and Macbeth (6)
18 Bird with prized plumes (5)
19 "___ in April never came so sweet" (4)
21 Intimidates (7)
22 "Ready, ___!" (5)
24 Electrical unit (3)
25 Nickname for late night's O'Brien (4)
26 Legal guarantees (3)
27 Caffeine or nicotine (5)
30 Burn-relieving plants (5)
31 Borges contemporary (3)
32 Conciliatory (4)
33 "Morning in America" pres. (3)
34 Suffix meaning inflamed (4)

Down

2   Till now (6)
3   One, to Antoine (3)
4   Congers (4)
5   Indian timber trees (4)
6   Feathered diver (4)
9   Pool competitions (5)
11 ". . . how I wonder what you ___" (3)
12 Earth color (5)
13 Landed group (6)
14 ___ special (6)
15 Causing wonder (9)
17 "I call 'em as I ___" (5)
20 Craftsman (7)
21 Gardener's supply (7)
23 Ham or Shakespearean (5)
25 Home of the Minoan civilization (5)
26 Gather up, as crops (4)
28 Floyd and Norman (4)
29 Big bad boss (4)

CROSSWORD 69

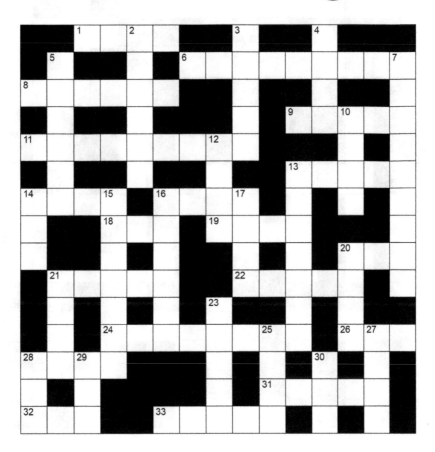

Across

1 Restless desire (4)
6 Words from an award winner (9)
8 Tasks to be done (6)
9 It may reflect well on you (5)
11 Rounded up? (9)
13 Pinza and Chaliapin. (5)
14 XXIX x C (4)
16 "___ Said" (song by the Shirelles) (4)
18 Begum's mate (3)
19 Unreserved (4)
20 Patch of pitch (3)
21 Diamond great with the line "I really didn't say everything I said" (5)
22 Opponent of Tom and Harry in 1948 (5)
24 Catering trays (8)
26 Image on some joke T-shirts (3)
28 Snick-or-____ (4)
31 Kid's comeback (5)
32 Justin Trudeau's party (3)
33 Edible (or inedible!) animal organs (5)

Down

2 Writing on the crawl? (6)
3 It lost out to "The English Patient" for Best Picture (5)
4 ___ Lomond (4)
5 ___ Investments (Boston-based financial company) (6)
7 Field dealing with bridges (9)
10 Handily, after "with" (4)
12 Prom night transport (4)
13 Holy City of the Hindus. (7)
14 Gas stat (3)
15 Ship-gangway handrail (7)
16 Shaking thing (6)
17 iPad purchases (4)
20 2007 film featuring Raphael, Leonardo, Donatello and Michelangelo (4)
21 Capital on the Aare (4)
23 Office personnel (5)
25 Third ___ (dangerous part of a subway track) (4)
27 Hero-type (4)
28 Comedy show letters (3)
29 Fall back, as a tide (3)
30 A giant of a Giant (3)

CROSSWORD 70

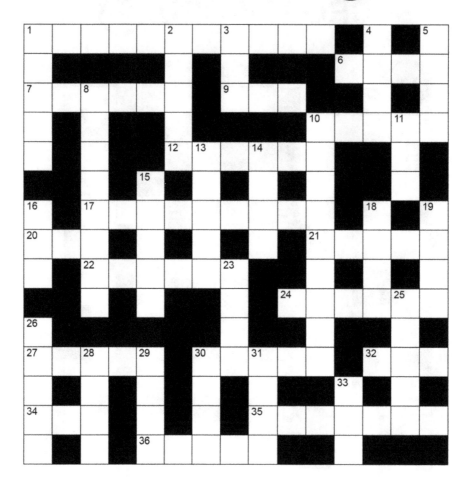

Across

1 Sweater selection? (11)
6 They may be shot in the open (4)
7 Ed of "Married...With Children" (6)
9 Thumbs down (3)
10 They know what's coming (5)
12 Came after (6)
17 Energy Star label bearer (9)
20 Magazine higher-ups, for short (3)
21 "Cute" sound (5)
22 Radio actress Rich et al. (6)
24 Religious rationalists (6)
27 "The Great White North" insult (5)
30 Available, in a way (5)
32 Sea monster (3)
34 __ Grande (part of Texas' border) (3)
35 'Ms.' pioneer (7)
36 Like non-oyster months? (5)

Down

1 Smokes once touted by Willie the penguin (5)
2 Eloper's acquisition (5)
3 Boy toy (3)
4 One with a neck and a lip (4)
5 Systems of principles (4)
8 Where Korea is (8)
10 Feature of many tires (9)
11 Volleyball arbiter (3)
13 Net mag (5)
14 __ place (4)
15 More northerly (5)
16 Important number on Downing Street (3)
18 Years in Madrid (4)
19 Club collection (4)
23 Farmland skyline highlight (4)
25 Unwordy (5)
26 When repeated, a comforting word (5)
28 Retail outlet (4)
29 Back part (4)
30 'Gypsy' star Daly (4)
31 What some settle for (4)
33 "__ the year's midnight ..." (3)

CROSSWORD 71

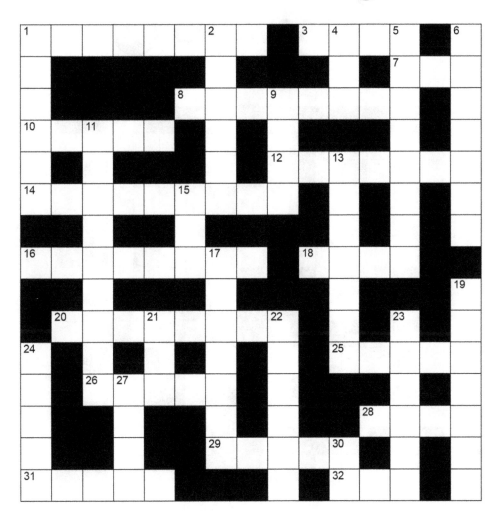

Across

1 Avows (8)
3 Not likely (4)
7 Urban rd. (3)
8 PR events (8)
10 Get married on the spur of the moment (5)
12 Now and again (7)
14 Things that turn people off? (9)
16 Suffer neglect (8)
18 "___ Bill" (2003) (4)
20 "Canciones de Mi Padre" singer (8)
25 Little pies baked by the Queen of Hearts (5)
26 Rice alternative (5)
28 Greek ruler of Syracuse (4)
29 Cut above the flank (5)
31 '50s Phileas Fogg portrayer (5)
32 Snagged (3)

Down

1 Conspiracy (6)
2 President Ahmadinejad's capital (6)
4 Cat constellation (3)
5 Campaign marketing strategy (8)
6 Bears witness (7)
9 They're high in the late afternoon (4)
11 Course served in a small crock (9)
13 Dark time? (7)
15 Late shipping tycoon's nickname (3)
17 Adhesive substance (7)
19 Heavily (7)
21 A.C.T. takers (3)
22 Pilot program? (6)
23 Whistler, but not his mother (6)
24 Off ___ (5)
27 "_____sow..." (4)
30 For example, abbr. (2)

CROSSWORD 72

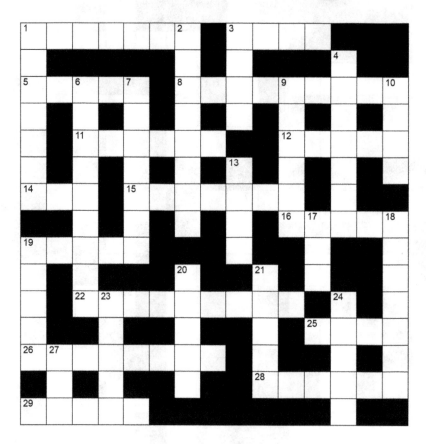

Across

1 Pit-crew "patient" (7)
3 ___ fever (be hot) (4)
5 Dutch pot contents (5)
8 1984 mockumentary subject (9)
11 Dokken "Burning Like ___" (6)
12 Mold particle (5)
14 ___ of the Mark, in S.F. (3)
15 British officials, to the colonists (7)
16 Capital on the Mediterranean (5)
19 Bottom-rung workers (5)
22 "Syndrome" that causes smartphone typos (9)
25 Muppet friend of Rosie (4)
26 Kiss, for the fancy (8)
28 Company that introduced Dramamine (6)
29 Tramped (5)

Down

1 Scott Adams rodent (7)
2 Leaves in the kitchen (8)
3 Santa's lead? (4)
4 Covered (for) (7)
6 Like a good travel mug (9)
7 Wine tasters' assets (7)
9 Court coup (6)
10 Near (4)
13 Rich fort (4)
17 Emmy-winning actress ___ Aduba of "Orange Is the New Black" (3)
18 Gelid treat (7)
19 Mickey Mouse's pet pooch (5)
20 Like Pluto, once (5)
21 Presidents' subordinates (5)
23 Critical (5)
24 Smartphone setting (5)
27 Enjoy a slope (3)

CROSSWORD 73

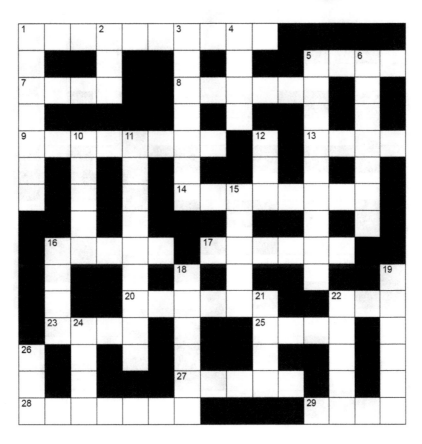

Across

1 Handle online (10)
5 Castor or Pollux, e.g. (4)
7 Whence the line "Let my people go" (4)
8 Character in "A Connecticut Yankee in King Arthur's Court" (6)
9 Business for manicurists? (8)
13 Duck's prominence (4)
14 Give up (8)
16 Armour's answer to Spam (5)
17 Coquettes (6)
20 Opened (or closed), as a shot on a set (6)
22 Gloria Estefan's "___ Mi Canto" (3)
23 Wild plum. (4)
25 Sounds that mice evoke (4)
27 Send money (5)
28 Gets coverage for (7)
29 Private school, briefly (4)

Down

1 He wrote "Alastor" (7)
2 Tackle's linemate (3)
3 Figure or symbol like '1', for example (7)
4 Report card notation (4)
5 Short-barreled (9)
6 Does an aquarium job (7)
10 Floor-care machine (5)
11 Latin motto for a go-getter (9)
12 Ginger ___ (bubbly drink) (3)
15 Nutmeg e.g. (5)
16 Finishes, as a road (4)
18 Pen fixtures? (6)
19 Baggage handler (6)
21 Lucy-___ Museum in Jamestown, N.Y. (4)
22 Award won by lead actors in this puzzle's starred films (5)
24 Ad-___ (improvises) (4)
26 "___ need to explain?" (3)

CROSSWORD 74

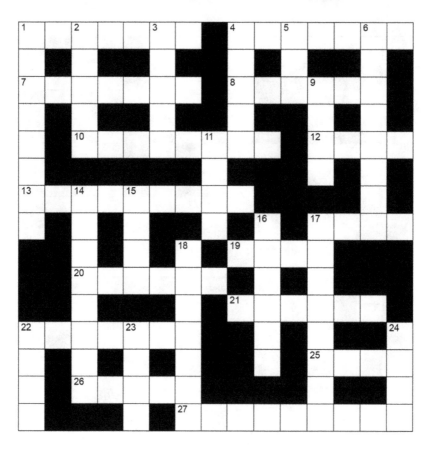

Across

1 Expand (7)
4 Revered sage, in India (7)
7 Be scintillating (7)
8 Orange road sign word (6)
10 Second of a double-header (8)
12 Cherry, for one (4)
13 Taking badly? (9)
17 Patronizing one (4)
19 Creator of Akbar and Jeff (4)
20 River along the Oregon Trail (6)
21 'The Deer Hunter' director (6)
22 Ancient Anatolian (7)
25 Retired NBA superstar ___ Bryant (4)
26 Rolls for lunch (5)
27 Tourist shop purchases (9)

Down

1 End of a plug, often (8)
2 Broil (5)
3 May or June, to Daisy Duck (5)
4 ___ Secretary (term of address for Hillary Clinton when she was Secretary of State) (5)
5 Asian stew often eaten with a dipping sauce (3)
6 Clothing impresario who bought Barry Bonds' record-breaking home run ball (8)
9 Palindromic fellow (4)
11 Soon, in sonnets (4)
14 Questions (8)
15 Havana's land (4)
16 Risqué (6)
17 Wounded (8)
18 Patron of Paris (7)
22 Bigfoot photo, e.g. (4)
23 '-- deal!' (4)
24 Takes to the altar (4)

CROSSWORD 75

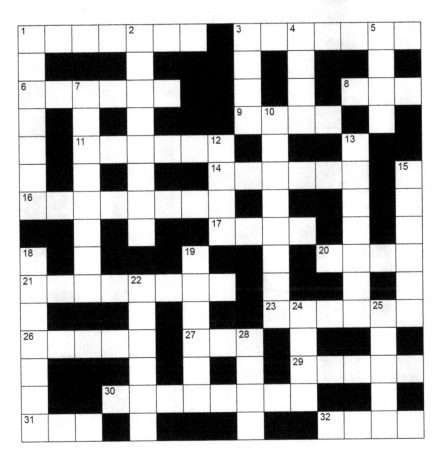

Across

1 Patriotic renditions (7)
3 Some West Point grads (7)
6 Slacken (6)
8 OK Corral nickname (3)
9 Targets of men who make passes (4)
11 Divides (6)
14 Turn one's back on (6)
16 Increased in depth (8)
17 On the other hand (4)
20 Ridge of sand created by the wind (4)
21 Gold medal winner (8)
23 Trees or nuts (6)
26 Word before ball or after figure (5)
27 "___ guy walks into a bar . . ." (joke start) (3)
29 La Scala features (5)
30 List holders (8)
31 "Holy moly," to a texter (3)
32 Mexican assents (4)

Down

1 "Historia Calamitatum" autobiographer (7)
2 Rivaled (8)
3 "Them that asks no questions isn't told __" (4)
4 Red or blue state? (4)
5 The i's have them (4)
7 Sub rosa (8)
10 Model of excellence (8)
12 Sports team (4)
13 Annexation (7)
15 Those who might get needled at work? (6)
18 Kia SUV (7)
19 Git down an' dirty? (6)
22 Poignancy (6)
24 New Testament book between John and Romans (4)
25 Fuzzy, as some monitor images (5)
28 PDQ relative (4)

CROSSWORD 76

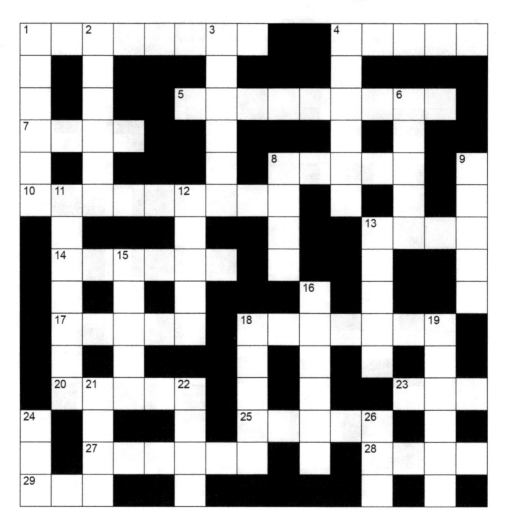

Across

1   Rides that aren't new (8)
4   Sounds relieved (5)
5   Comic's employee (9)
7   Innkeeper, in Italy (4)
8   Odds opposite (5)
10   Cereal that's partly ground? (9)
13   Keyway. (4)
14   Deep sleeps (6)
17   Ambles and others (5)
18   Encounters, with "with" (7)
20   Galts (5)
23   Frodo pursuer (3)
25   Wheat sold in health-food stores (5)
27   Enjoy perfume (6)
28   Took ___ (snoozed) (4)
29   Pet food container (3)

Down

1   Do a longshoreman's job (6)
2   Marginal worker? (6)
3   Anthology (6)
4   Homophone for a Roman (6)
6   Citation or Corsair (5)
8   Olympic Stadium athlete (4)
9   Whale of a constellation? (5)
11   Perception (7)
12   Some lawnmowers (5)
13   Type of Latin music (5)
15   ___ Vance, fictional sleuth (5)
16   Pressed the juice out (6)
18   Click-and-drag device (5)
19   Bookie's concern (6)
21   Total (4)
22   Zest, e.g. (4)
24   "King" Steve Martin sang about (3)
26   Russian chess great (3)

CROSSWORD 77

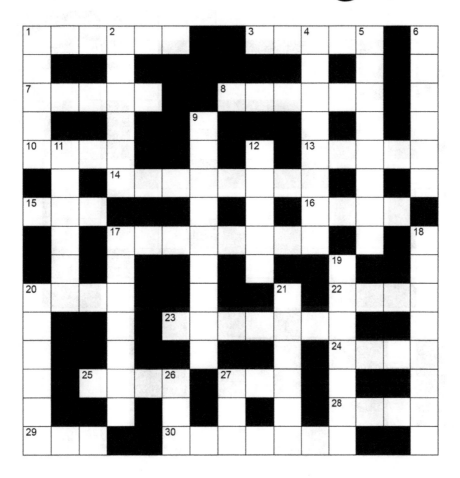

Across

1 Robert Guillaume series (6)
3 Traces (5)
7 Sometimes-branded animal (5)
8 French "Va-va-voom!" (6)
10 Home to Ellsworth A.F.B. (4)
13 Place for some durable furniture (5)
14 "Dunno" (8)
15 Prefix with "brow" (3)
16 Be tough on the nose (4)
17 Turkey cookers (8)
20 Run for potential customers (4)
22 Rainbow Man's hairdo (4)
23 Damp state (7)
24 Lake Erie neighbor (4)
25 NL franchise (4)
27 High-school subj. (3)
28 Pod part, perhaps (4)
29 Hand tool with teeth (3)
30 River duck (7)

Down

1 Cable managers, for short (5)
2 Gives an address (6)
4 Astor employes (8)
5 TV show with the most spinoffs, according to the Guinness Book (8)
6 Help with a cover story, say (6)
9 It was captured by British forces in 1917 (9)
11 Strip off covering (6)
12 Rip to pieces (5)
17 Cornelius, on Corn Flakes boxes (7)
18 What this puzzle is, really (8)
19 Alternative fuel (7)
20 First showings (6)
21 Aunt known for breakfasts (6)
26 Potent hallucinogen (3)
27 _____ Clemente (3)

CROSSWORD 78

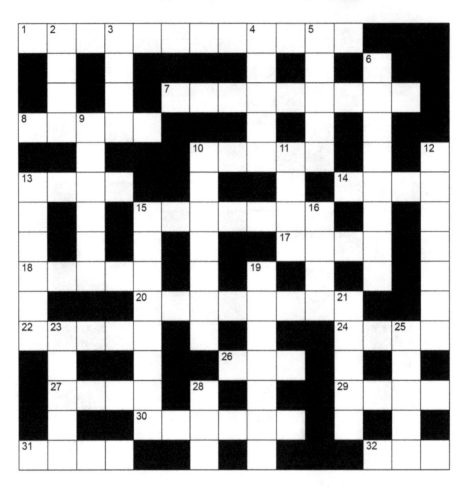

Across

1 Tulip tree (12)
7 Calming drugs (9)
8 Painter's preparation (5)
10 "Oh! What a girl!" girl of song (5)
13 Adam's first (4)
14 River rising in the Ardennes (4)
15 Overall chief (7)
17 Biting stingers (4)
18 Lava, while underground (5)
20 Detective superintendent Jane of TV's "Prime Suspect" (8)
22 Mountain for Moses (5)
24 "___ de Castro" (John Clifford play) (4)
26 CFL stats (3)
27 Dizzy of baseball (4)
29 Tale start (4)
30 Electric razor (6)
31 Greek administrative area (4)
32 Dream stage (3)

Down

2 "The NeverEnding Story" author Michael (4)
3 Is dishonest, in a way (4)
4 Looks to the future (5)
5 Fragrant seed (5)
6 Most intoxicated? (8)
9 Aspen attraction (6)
10 Castrato's register, perhaps (7)
11 Friend in a 1949 film (4)
12 Night flights (7)
13 Emulates Hillary (6)
15 Union and Penn (8)
16 Norwegian Nobel Institute locale (4)
19 Piano student's key note (7)
21 Savor of cooking. (5)
23 Sundance entry, often (5)
25 Modern traveler's purchase (5)
28 Calico, for one (3)

CROSSWORD 79

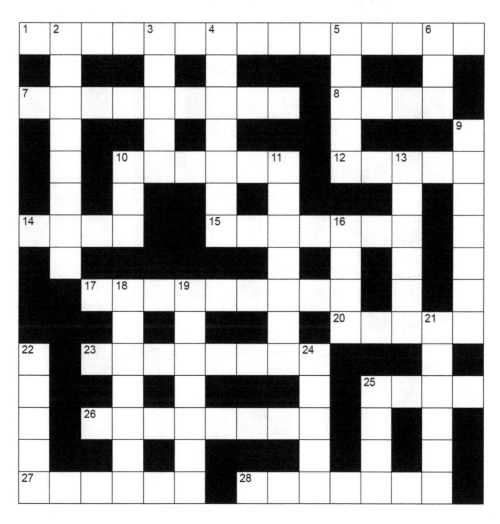

Across

1 Linus' trademark in "Peanuts" comics (15)
7 Likewise (9)
8 Australian mine yield (4)
10 Fabric with holes (6)
12 Condor's roost (5)
14 Corleone creator (4)
15 Watched furtively (7)
17 Word from the Greek for "equal-legged" (9)
20 Targets of inflation (5)
23 Divisions (8)
25 Icebox incursion (4)
26 Ten-year periods (8)
27 Houston team that became the Tennessee Titans (6)
28 Annoying biter, informally (7)

Down

2 Struggling to get (8)
3 Pass on (5)
4 Hard-shelled creatures (7)
5 Plaza for Plato (5)
6 New wing (3)
9 Removes impurities from (7)
10 Alternative to metal (3)
11 "Uncivil Liberties" columnist (7)
13 Tried to catch (6)
16 Houseclean (4)
18 "You listen to me" (7)
19 Family room pieces, sometimes (7)
21 Magical drink (6)
22 Horn honker of film (5)
24 Extra (5)
25 Wild retreat (4)

CROSSWORD 80

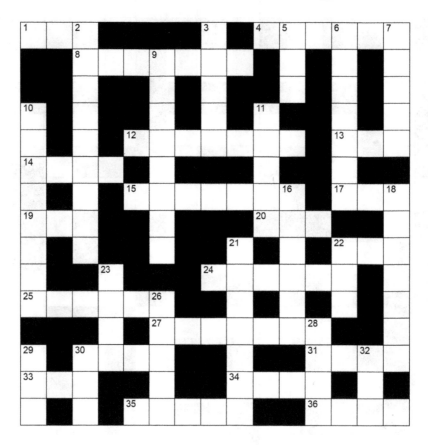

Across

1 Folklore sprite (3)
4 Feature of some cell phones (6)
8 Exterminators often kill them (7)
12 Crop with a powerful Washington lobby (7)
13 Amsterdam of l'Océan Indien, e.g. (3)
14 Thatching material (4)
15 Old prospector (7)
17 Diplomatic hdqrs. (3)
19 Eastern sch. with a noted film program (3)
20 Medal (3)
22 Lining for some coats (3)
24 Japanese auto (6)
25 Channel changer (6)
27 Superior floor, e.g. (7)
30 ___-bellum. (4)
31 The middle Karamazov brother (4)
33 Pete Seeger "Never ___ an Old Man" (3)
34 Frat initiation, for one (4)
35 Roof edges that gutters are attached to (5)
36 Bottom topper? (4)

Down

2 Shower and change, say (9)
3 Birthplace of Christopher Columbus (5)
5 TV's Baker (3)
6 Structure (7)
7 Sherman who coached the Giants (5)
9 Pertaining to the heart (8)
10 TV host Jerry (8)
11 Two quartets (5)
16 ___ fly (6)
18 1974 Best Actress for "Alice Doesn't Live Here Anymore" (7)
21 Space rocks (7)
22 Mis' neighbors (3)
23 Wheat, in England (4)
26 High court's Kagan (5)
28 Reducer's regimen (4)
29 Monogram of the author of "A Charge to Keep (3)
30 ___ to Cart (Amazon button) (3)
32 Parts 7 and 11 of today 's quote (3)

CROSSWORD 81

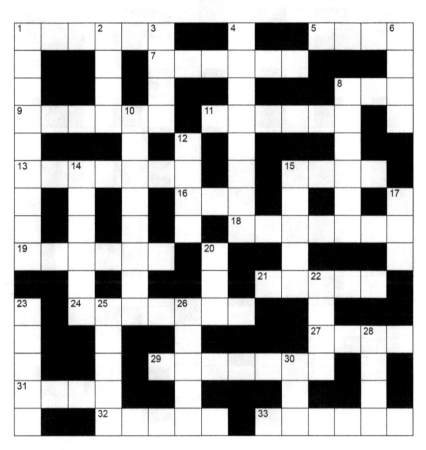

Across

1 Gazed wantonly (6)
5 Al Capp's hyena (4)
7 In a light way (6)
8 Ref's ring ruling (3)
9 Movement concerned with crystals (6)
11 Knight's collie (6)
13 Yearly calendar (7)
15 Brief denial (4)
16 ___ Direction ("Story of My Life" band) (3)
18 Pedal-to-the-metal type (7)
19 Back column? (6)
21 Stroll like a cowpoke (5)
24 Input, as accidentally erased data (7)
27 Kong and Young (4)
29 Church seat (7)
31 Snowthrower manufacturer (4)
32 Place for a light slap (5)
33 Spells of duty (6)

Down

1 One-time picnic game (9)
2 Name of a 1988 country album and a 2001 sitcom (4)
3 Florida county (4)
4 Money matters (8)
6 Run ___ (go berserk) (4)
8 Checked (6)
10 Make (8)
12 Kind of free (4)
14 More depressed (6)
15 ___ Laredo, Mexico (5)
17 Tantalite, e.g. (3)
20 Member of the familia (3)
22 One of the deer hunters in "The Deer Hunter" (4)
23 Hit for rapper Yung L.A. (5)
25 Funny-bone locale (5)
26 Milk dispensers (5)
28 ___ St. Louis, IL (4)
30 Collage, e.g. (3)

CROSSWORD 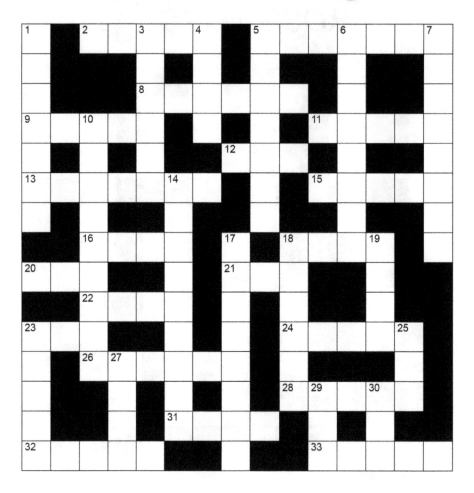82

Across

2   Crude cabin (5)
5   Bit of cocoa? (7)
8   Charger of interest (6)
9   "--- Was a Lady" (1932 song) (5)
11 Estate home (5)
12 File format for some pics (3)
13 Like rock stars among fans (7)
15 Treasured instrument (5)
16 Mexicali's locale (4)
18 1985 Grammy winner for Best New Artist (4)
20 "Didn't I tell ya?" (3)
21 Eggs of eels (3)
22 Start for dynamic or nautical (4)
23 Retired fast plane (abbr.) (3)
24 P.D. James product (5)
26 Overexert (6)
28 An in-law (5)
31 Fish with lethal pulses (4)
32 Potpourri output (5)
33 Forehead coverings (5)

Down

1   Backward (7)
3   Radiant (6)
4   Hawaii's coffee belt (4)
5   A spire is part of one (7)
6   Mummified (8)
7   Chicken Little, notably (8)
10 Party spongers (9)
14 Give details (9)
17 Mutineers' targets (8)
18 Occult activity (6)
19 Suffix for depend (4)
23 Grunting tennis legend (5)
25 Papua New Guinea port in W.W. II news (3)
27 Mall denizen (4)
29 Pointed end (3)
30 Fawn, e.g. (3)

CROSSWORD 83

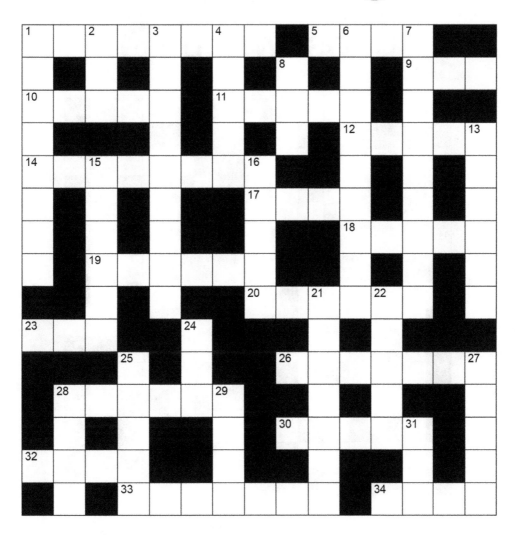

Across

1 One of 46 in the Senate. (8)
5 Sizes above meds. (4)
9 Iconic beret-wearing revolutionary (3)
10 Give license (5)
11 Nuisance in an online comments section (5)
12 Cygnus's brightest (5)
14 It's not a rodent (8)
17 Kind of boots (4)
18 Troy, by another name (5)
19 Eases off (6)
20 Surprising plot turns (6)
23 On the canvas, informally (3)
26 Enjoys a favorite book (7)
28 Henley entries (6)
30 Bugs' bugbear (5)
32 Perfected, in the wine cellar (4)
33 Kind of cat (7)
34 Certain incentive (4)

Down

1 Carnation genus (8)
2 "Braveheart" star Gibson (3)
3 Top of a range? (9)
4 Cultural doings in Cádiz (5)
6 Hanukkah candy shapes (9)
7 Outlines (9)
8 Mayday signal (3)
13 Smiled for the camera (6)
15 Dressed for a frat party? (6)
16 Discharge through the pores (5)
21 Perfectly (7)
22 '-- it is!' (5)
24 "That's not ___" (3)
25 Documents (5)
27 Watery snow (5)
28 Big story (4)
29 Acrab or Acrux (4)
31 Royal Military Academy, abbr. (3)

CROSSWORD 84

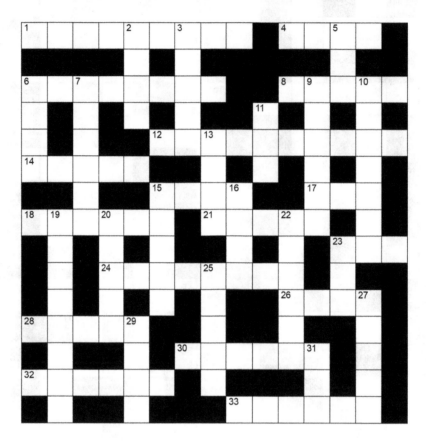

Across

1 Mulish (9)
4 Lose strength (4)
6 Antipasto veggie (8)
8 2018 US Open winner Osaka (5)
12 Top-of-the-line (10)
14 Boost (5)
15 A marmoset (4)
17 "Keep on Loving You" ___ Speedwagon (3)
18 Pelion neighbor (6)
21 "___ to sew . . . " (5)
23 P.R., for one (3)
24 Alee's opposite (8)
26 Belfry occupants (4)
28 Elephant's quartet (5)
30 Deeply impressed (6)
32 Not as well-done (6)
33 Drinking toast (6)

Down

2 What a light bulb might symbolize (4)
3 "Space mutt" in the early 1980s cartoon "Space Stars" (5)
5 Shortest zodiac sign, lexically (3)
6 Plumbing item (4)
7 Gilbert _Sullivan title character (6)
9 Certain appeal (6)
10 Mr. Met and the Phillie Phanatic, e.g. (7)
11 Tally one's scorecard (3)
13 Lovely ticketer of song (4)
15 Worker with circus lions (5)
16 Calamine lotion target (4)
19 Recent hires (8)
20 Cabinet department (5)
22 Shooter of a sort (6)
23 It's often compounded (3)
25 Brightly colored fish (5)
27 Tchaikovsky ballet birds (5)
29 Court participant (4)
31 Nevada's largest county by area (3)

CROSSWORD 85

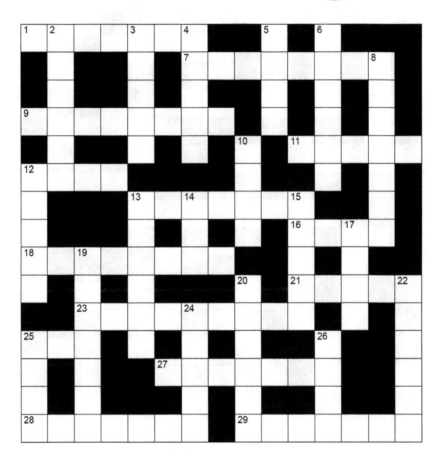

Across

1 Roundup ropes (7)
7 "Stop being such a baby!" (8)
9 Holy higher-ups (8)
11 Pakistani money (5)
12 Televisions (4)
13 Stresses (7)
16 Seems reasonable, with "up" (4)
18 Some music-box activity (8)
21 "Till ___ Was You," 1957 song (5)
23 Fifth gear, often (9)
25 Chinese calendar animal (3)
27 Enlists (7)
28 More rapid (7)
29 Of this world (7)

Down

2 Renee of films (6)
3 Alternative handle (5)
4 Not sozzled (5)
5 Street urchin (4)
6 Like some Disneyland passes (6)
8 Continues (7)
10 Villainess Vanderwaal of TV's "Pretty Little Liars" (4)
12 Cues for typesetters (5)
13 Nations joining together (6)
14 Cell occupant (3)
15 "A votre ___" (5)
17 "Go put your creed into your ___" (4)
19 Protium, for one (7)
20 One with encumbered property (6)
22 Currency you can't hold (6)
24 Not so damp (5)
25 It might be just below the surface (4)
26 RPI or MIT (4)

CROSSWORD 86

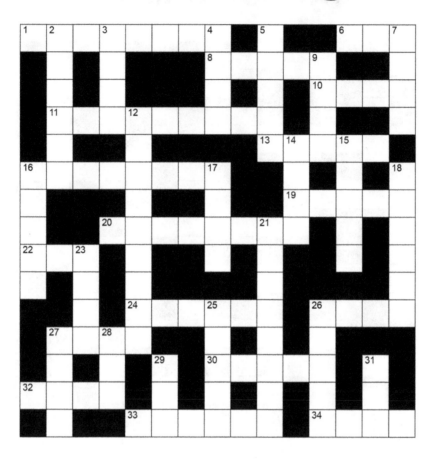

Across

1 Screen patterns (8)
6 Bounced-check letters (3)
8 Like a supportive crowd (5)
10 Roll-call calls (4)
11 Possible strain cause (9)
13 Dictionary label (5)
16 Anticipatory question (8)
19 Canal Zone lake (5)
20 Old-line types (8)
22 Le contraire de "oui" (3)
24 Cake (6)
26 Pulitzer-winning columnist Herb (4)
27 Goat-drawn chariot rider, in myth (4)
30 ___ a customer (sale limit) (5)
32 Phototropic flier (4)
33 Beam connectors (6)
34 Parted parties (4)

Down

2 "The Doors of Perception" author Huxley (6)
3 Gift wrapper's adhesive (4)
4 "The Twilight ___" (vampire film series starring Kristen Stewart) (4)
5 Lomond and Ness, for two (5)
7 Suffix for slug or song (4)
9 An incarnation of Vishnu (4)
12 Dog (9)
14 Diamond in the rough? (4)
15 Trim (5)
16 Armenian's neighbor (5)
17 Page sent by computer (4)
18 Like Carlton the doorman on "Rhoda" (6)
21 Queries (8)
23 Impending (4)
25 Left a chair (5)
26 ___ hitch, nautical knot. (5)
27 Fun run pace (4)
28 "I'm impressed!" (3)
29 Popular TV crime show (3)
31 "That's interesting" (3)

CROSSWORD 87

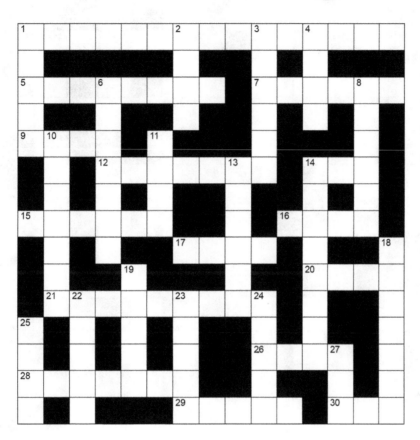

Across

1. Computer store section (15)
5. Beach scuttler (8)
7. Displays of military power, for short (6)
9. Org. with peacekeeping forces (4)
12. Parachutist's need (7)
14. Piper of myth (3)
15. ___ valve (part of an engine) (6)
16. Netlike fabric (4)
17. Redo some passages, maybe (4)
20. In-box filler, perhaps (4)
21. Very sad (9)
26. War maker (4)
28. Frequent fly-ball catcher (7)
29. Roy's wife Dale (5)
30. ___ Holiness Pope Francis (3)

Down

1. He had a supporting role alongside Hepburn in "Breakfast at Tiffany's" (5)
2. Words with equal basis or empty stomach (4)
3. Aslope (6)
4. Hemsley TV vehicle (4)
6. Carlton, in "Rhoda" (7)
8. Coat type (6)
10. Got even (7)
11. Setback at church? (4)
13. Staff after a furlough, say (6)
14. Stress (8)
18. Western and cheese dishes (7)
19. Kept. Asking. More. And. More. Questions. (5)
22. Wasn't renewed (5)
23. Brit's blade (5)
24. Unsheathed (5)
25. Two-legged zebras (4)
27. Academy (abbr.) (3)

CROSSWORD 88

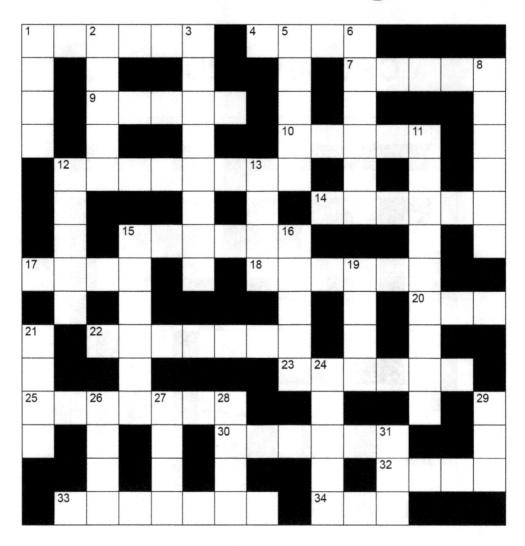

Across

1 Vegetable with greens (6)
4 Vaudeville bit (4)
7 Late Fox News CEO Roger (5)
9 Dr. Venkman of "Ghostbusters" (5)
10 Utah ski locale (5)
12 Something to see on the first day of school (8)
14 ____ emptor (6)
15 Sword case (6)
17 Sundown direction (4)
18 Brothers' keepers? (6)
20 "Listen up!" (3)
22 He's out of this world (7)
23 Prolific inventor (6)
25 __ hydrate (7)
30 View blocker (6)
32 Famous reproach (4)
33 Talk and talk and ... (7)
34 Prog band that turns 40 in 2008 (3)

Down

1 Mediator's skill (4)
2 Currency in Nepal (5)
3 Ready (8)
5 Single-serving coffee pods (5)
6 City just south of Seattle (6)
8 Type of bond (6)
11 Go beyond, as a target (9)
12 Hard-__ (5)
13 Place of fiction (4)
15 Platter player (6)
16 A cut of beef (5)
19 Present and potent leader (4)
21 "An American Tail" critters (4)
24 Slow (5)
26 Person not telling it like it is (4)
27 Spring outlook (4)
28 Entertaining Jay (4)
29 Fresh, in Frankfurt (3)
31 Hôtel ____ Invalides (3)

CROSSWORD 89

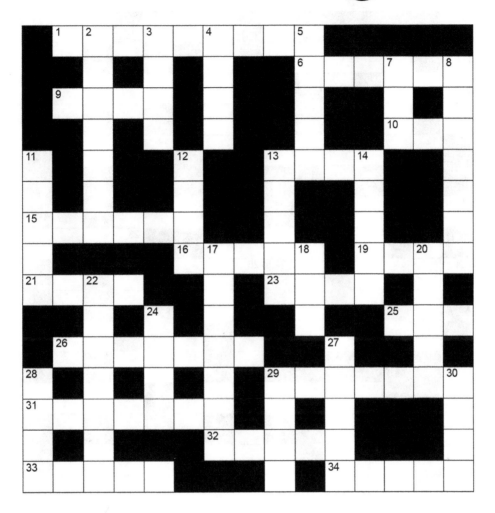

Across

1   Measurers (9)
6   Fast starter (6)
9   "Let's ___ a Deal" (4)
10   Nautical chain (3)
13   Beachgoers get them (4)
15   "How to Argue and Win Every Time" author (6)
16   High dudgeon (5)
19   End of a chess game (4)
21   Cylindrical storage structure (4)
23   Bar in a dish (4)
25   "veryfunny" cable network (3)
26   Home of Glacier National Park (7)
29   Rearrangement of letters (7)
31   Bikers' wear, often (7)
32   Eucalypts (5)
33   Totaled up (5)
34   White House architect James (5)

Down

2   In fashion — served with ice cream (7)
3   Nonstop (4)
4   "--- have to do" (4)
5   Memorial at a Buddhist wat (5)
7   "Great ___," 1929 song (3)
8   Film star's trailers (7)
11   Elephant teeth (5)
12   Just some (4)
13   Grassy clumps (5)
14   Bit of philately (5)
17   Part of an Apollo mission (7)
18   Soil-shaping tool (3)
20   Small drum of India (5)
22   Composer ____ Bernstein (7)
24   A state carved out of Deseret (4)
27   Like winters in the Arctic (5)
28   Pot, in Potosí (4)
29   Lead-in to "boy" or "girl" (4)
30   "I ___ business!" (4)

CROSSWORD 90

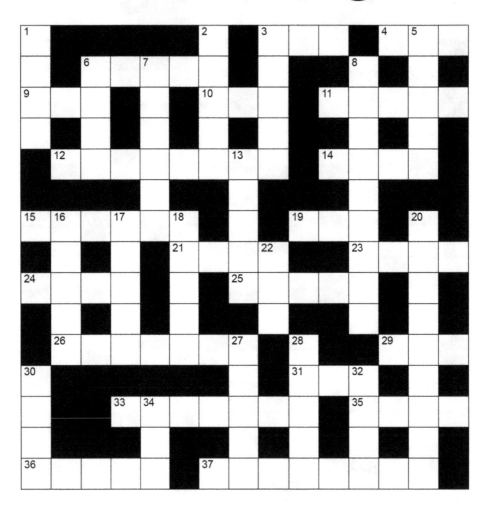

Across

3 Celebrated Bruin blueliner (3)
4 It's not done on a DNR patient (3)
6 Spoil, as an egg (5)
9 Boxing biopic (3)
10 Supplement (3)
11 Timorous (5)
12 Kind of sweater (8)
14 Little chief hare (4)
15 Ain't That ___? (6)
19 Record label inits. (3)
21 Japanese legislature (4)
23 Bud (4)
24 Show sorrow or joy (4)
25 Israel's neighbor (5)
26 Quick witty reply (7)
29 Green marker (3)
31 Some, in Somme (3)
33 Family with three generations of Oscar winners (7)
35 On the nose (4)
36 Far from cordial (5)
37 Adjust to a new home (8)

Down

1 Common drink assortment (4)
2 Measures up to (5)
3 A daisy. (5)
5 Ottoman honorific (5)
6 Opera that debuted in Cairo in 1871 (4)
7 Ph or ey, e.g. (6)
8 Kind of system (9)
13 Decoys, for example (5)
16 Missy Higgins song about driving? (5)
17 Excite, in slang (5)
18 Where ice skates meet the ice (5)
20 Reproduction (9)
22 Heisman winner Detmer et al. (3)
27 Have a secret wedding (5)
28 In ___ (seeing stars, perhaps) (5)
30 Computer software (4)
32 Leave in, in editing (4)
34 Kind of color (3)

CROSSWORD 91

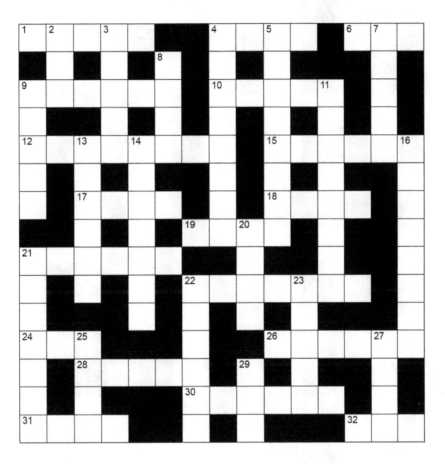

Across

1 2003 Sigourney Weaver movie (5)
4 Feeling one's oats (4)
6 Bizet's buddy (3)
9 Salma Hayek or Sofía Vergara (6)
10 Hannah Montana, to Miley Stewart (5)
12 Polite words of interruption (8)
15 Wound (around) (6)
17 It borders Sask. (4)
18 Item once thought indivisible (4)
19 Hunch over (4)
21 Fortunetelling aids (6)
22 The Rebels (7)
24 It's ignored in "alphabétisation" (3)
26 Cure "___ (6)
28 Slide specimen (5)
30 One of the Four Seasons (6)
31 Major quiz (4)
32 Magazine execs. (3)

Down

2 900-plus-mile Volga feeder (3)
3 ___ Root, Nobelist for Peace (5)
4 Be vulturous (8)
5 Convict unfairly (8)
7 Shortsighted one (5)
8 Cooked less than well or medium (4)
9 Santa-like (5)
11 Sex hormones, etc. (8)
13 Likely prospects (6)
14 Capitol Hill figure (7)
16 Wretched existence (8)
20 Door-to-door December ditty (4)
21 Person or thing similar to another (7)
22 Cold capital (6)
23 About to go through the roof (5)
25 Heroic narrative (4)
27 Sortie, say (4)
29 Show with a "Weekend Update" segment, briefly (3)

CROSSWORD 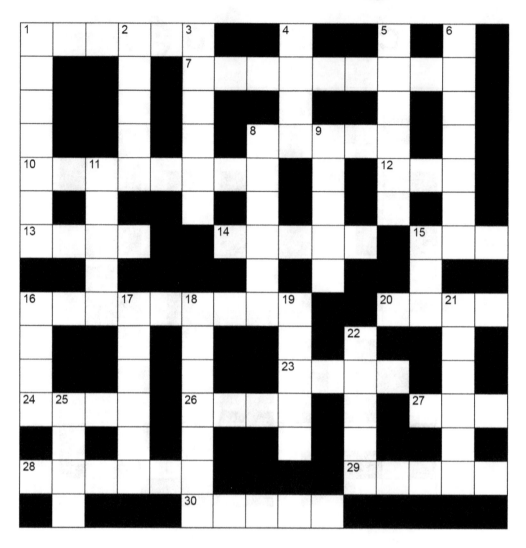92

Across

1 Fits of activity (6)
7 Get one's bearings (9)
8 Law experts (5)
10 Not as the crow flies (8)
12 Photo ___ (publicity events) (3)
13 "It Ain't All About the Cookin'" memoirist (4)
14 Brand endorsed by Michael Jordan (5)
15 Bob Marley used a "Small" one (3)
16 Performer with a whip (9)
20 Dotted, as porcelain (4)
23 Nickname of the singer of 2007's "Umbrella" (4)
24 Girds up (4)
26 Norse collection of poems (4)
27 Serpent follower (3)
28 Lead provider (6)
29 Subject of much poesia (5)
30 Ducks (5)

Down

1 Gannet or petrel (7)
2 Cuneiform implements (5)
3 Game that's not hands-on (6)
4 Lapel grabber (4)
5 Cause (6)
6 Chuck (7)
8 Drilling order (6)
9 Ambitious personality type (5)
11 Mural painter Rivera (5)
15 Beverage. (3)
16 Southern Italian village (4)
17 River to Oder (6)
18 "___ Ashes" (7)
19 Far from the big city (5)
21 Hungarian playwright (6)
22 Ornamental palm. (5)
25 1989 B-52's hit (4)

CROSSWORD 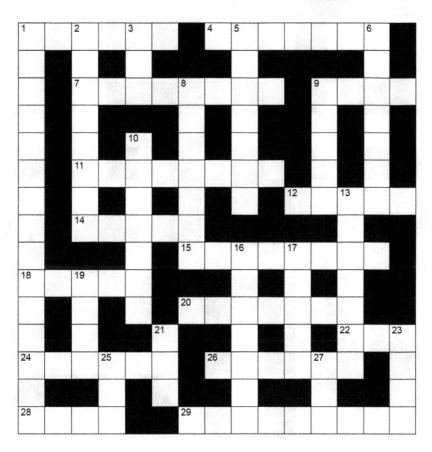 93

Across

1 QB Johnny (6)
4 Costume balls (7)
7 At the side of the path? (8)
9 "Now __ me down to sleep ..." (4)
11 1954 Edgar Award winner (8)
12 Dow's publishing partner (5)
14 Major functions (5)
15 Urban renewal targets (8)
18 Sexologist Havelock ___ (5)
20 Wet suits (7)
22 Ending for rocket or racket (3)
24 Folk singer and civil rights activist usually referred to by her first name (6)
26 How some park (6)
28 Scottish physicist John (4)
29 Catchphrase for a monkey with its eyes covered (9)

Down

1 Book that's not out yet (15)
2 Partaking of alcohol (8)
3 Creative talent (3)
5 1992 Disney film featuring a magic lamp (7)
6 Walk with an awkward gait (7)
8 Iran-contra figure (7)
9 "My name is ___ Montoya... You killed my father..." (5)
10 High to the max (7)
13 Cheap Trick guitarist Rick (7)
16 Neighborhood improvement target (7)
17 Doo-wop tune, say (5)
19 ___ duck (4)
21 Team encourager (3)
23 Cuban leader between Fidel and Miguel (4)
25 Dark viscous substance (3)
27 "___ noticed" (3)

CROSSWORD 94

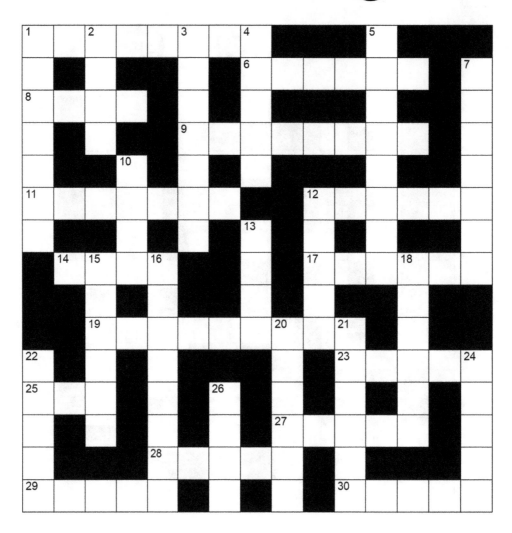

Across

1 They're stuck on themselves (8)
6 Fluoxetine hydrochloride, familiarly (6)
8 Dictionary abbr. (4)
9 Chased (8)
11 Pastry from Germany (7)
12 Brightest star in the Eagle constellation (6)
14 Revolutionary general (4)
17 Sweat ... hormones ... thyroid (6)
19 Top of the world (9)
23 One who may be "adorkable" (5)
25 Ones calling the shots, for short? (3)
27 1954 event coded as "Castle Bravo" (5)
28 Second-generation Japanese in the U.S. (5)
29 ___ course (at the right time) (5)
30 Uses a straw, maybe (5)

Down

1 Catherine the Great, to Russia (7)
2 Benediction opener (4)
3 Make more stylish (7)
4 Drained of energy (5)
5 Breaks, in Britain (8)
7 Corrida types (7)
10 Swat was his sultanate (4)
12 Illusionist Criss ___ (5)
13 Ferry terminus (4)
15 More clear-headed (6)
16 Kind of jack (8)
18 "Cat Scratch Fever" musician (6)
20 Showy flower (6)
21 Short-lived '50s sedans (6)
22 Of Iran (5)
24 Crunchy salad topping (5)
26 Hindu slave (4)

CROSSWORD 95

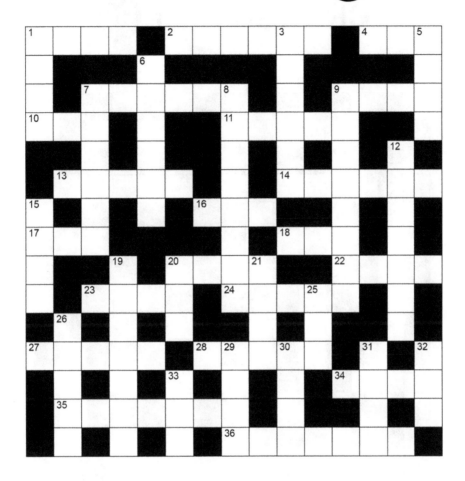

Across

1 The Aragon flows into it (4)
2 Japanese pilgrimage destination (6)
4 Film like "Rocky" (3)
7 "___ McNasty" (UPN TV series) (6)
9 One shaken to seal a deal (4)
10 Response to an oversharer (3)
11 Pointer Sisters "__ Shy" (5)
13 Channel that broadcasts Congressional hearings (5)
14 Japanese leader of yore (6)
16 Defib operator (3)
17 Ending with hallow (3)
18 Gas station purchase (3)
20 TV host Lauer (4)
22 Jon's comics canine (4)
23 Bull fiddle (4)
24 Meet component (5)
27 "It's on the level!" (5)
28 Diameters halved (5)
34 Pedro's pittance (4)
35 First words of "Saint Louis Blues" (7)
36 Looking good? (7)

Down

1 Fix a text (4)
3 Tilts in a match (6)
5 All alternative (4)
6 What regulars run up (6)
7 Keeps warm, as nest eggs (6)
8 Novelty seafood restaurant greeting (8)
9 Seuss book about destroying a kitchen item? (8)
12 "Turandot" composer (7)
15 Senate stretch (4)
19 It's often stopped on the street (7)
20 Food additive (3)
21 Spot on the air? (4)
25 Team feature? (3)
26 Picture show (5)
29 Tuneful Tori (4)
30 Early state in presidential campaigns (4)
31 Attica accommodation (4)
32 Signal to the auctioneer (3)
33 Major ref. set (3)

CROSSWORD 96

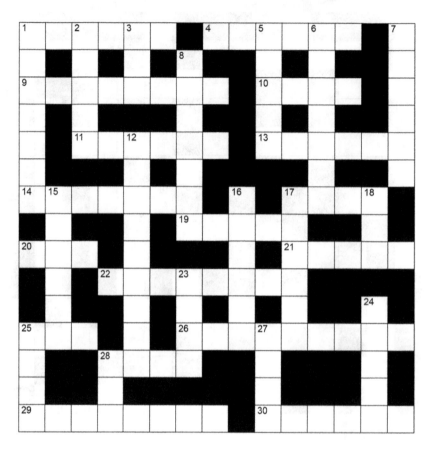

Across

1 Bygone currency (6)
4 Vigorous clash (6)
9 Really worked up (8)
10 Bahrain's ruler (4)
11 TV character Remington (6)
13 Dome covering (6)
14 Expose and destroy (7)
17 Rick on the radio (4)
19 Inventor Pliny ___ (5)
20 Do the seam thing (3)
21 Shelter, as in a cove (5)
22 Start, as a conversation (8)
25 High-speed Internet service (3)
26 "Candle in the Wind" singer [1998] (9)
28 Lucy Montgomery character (4)
29 Hang back (8)
30 Betty or Barney (6)

Down

1 He played Mister Tibbs (7)
2 They can be grand (5)
3 Jovial question from someone eager to help (3)
5 Kind of basil (5)
6 Idle hours (7)
7 Nighttime shindig (6)
8 Any Olympics competitor (7)
12 Toymaking center? (9)
15 Immense expanses (6)
16 East Asia (6)
17 Extend farther down (6)
18 '50s song syllable (3)
23 "Oh, O.K." (4)
24 Con artist's plant (5)
25 Make a run for it (4)
27 Van Halen "The Dream is ___" (4)
28 He said "If you even dream of beating me, you'd better wake up and apologize" (3)

CROSSWORD 97

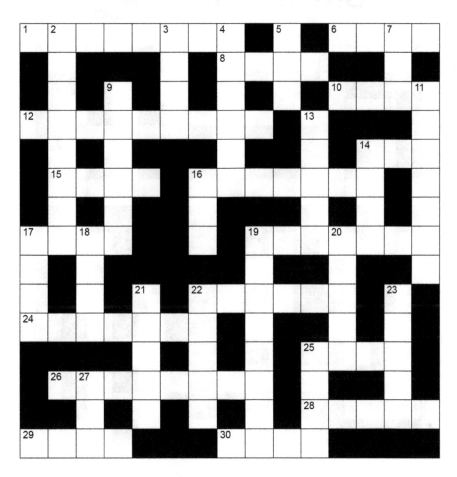

Across

1 Depicted faithfully (8)
6 Title of the first Fabergé egg owner (4)
8 Actress Macpherson (4)
10 ___ dog (husky or malamute, for example) (4)
12 Fast food snack (9)
14 Span in years (3)
15 Lifeguard's concern (4)
16 TV drama length (7)
17 "The Twelve Days of Christmas" gift (4)
19 Popular kitchen color of the '70s (7)
22 Bit of trail mix (6)
24 Sinister stare (7)
25 Latin word in legal briefs (4)
26 Natural inclination (8)
28 More likely to cause skidding (5)
29 "___ me your ears" (4)
30 '30s building style (4)

Down

2 Gilbert and Sullivan opera (8)
3 Lion's cry (4)
4 Lower. (6)
5 Degree for an att. (3)
7 Tapped tipple (3)
9 Hogans, igloos, etc. (6)
11 Refuse to let go of (7)
13 Thrifty, in brand names (5)
14 Vicinity (4)
16 Scrap from supper (3)
17 Try to avoid being found (4)
18 The Soup ___ (classic "Seinfeld" character) (4)
19 Espresso garnish (8)
20 Hit the bottom? (5)
21 National competitor (5)
22 Metaphor for management (5)
23 Greedy one's cry (5)
25 Of the pelvis (4)
27 Mother Teresa was one (3)

CROSSWORD 98

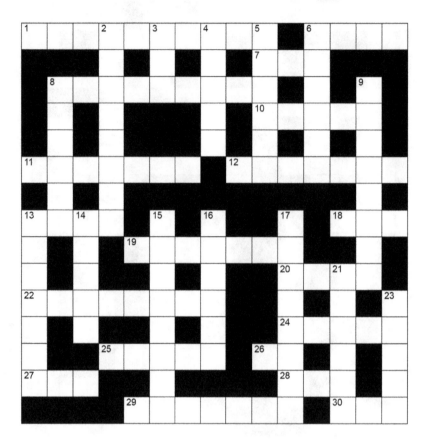

Across

1   Bar mitzvah suit material, perhaps? (10)
6   ___ rea (criminal intent) (4)
7   Half of deux (3)
8   Red wine variety (9)
10 Chive's cousin (5)
11 Former NPR show, or a description of the starred answers (7)
12 Pink, e.g. (7)
13 Tip follower (4)
18 Went under cover (3)
19 Subject of the 1997 best seller "Into Thin Air" (7)
20 Love, Latin-style (4)
22 Shortened (8)
24 Durango maker (5)
25 A solution's concentration (5)
26 Post grad degree (2)
27 1991-'96 Indian prime minister (3)
28 Erstwhile Atlantic crosser (3)
29 List (7)
30 Kurosawa's "King Lear" (3)

Down

2   Darkly evil (8)
3   Jet that was retired in 2003 (3)
4   Causes to bring out the National Guard (5)
5   Figure in Greek myth after whom a continent is named (6)
6   Stress-reduction period (6)
8   Easily bent (6)
9   Domestic (8)
13 Stanley's car (7)
14 Sugar Ray smash "___ Morning" (5)
15 "Thanks for explaining" (8)
16 It's often rocked (6)
17 It's not measured in traditional years (8)
21 Exclamation (6)
23 Large car (5)

CROSSWORD 99

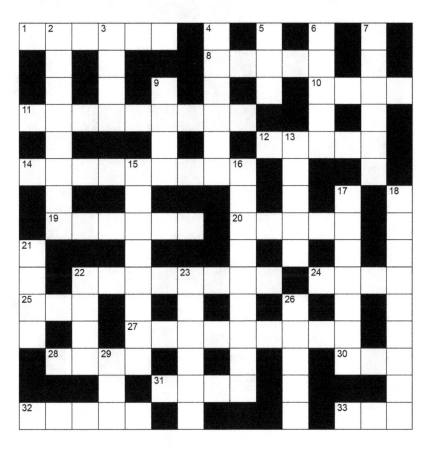

Across

1 They might make cats pause (6)
8 Evade (tax) (5)
10 Subject of a memorable chocolate simile (4)
11 Burger successor (9)
12 The Great Garbo (5)
14 Coastline (anag) (9)
19 Florida city that was once home to the world's largest Shuffleboard club (6)
20 ___ around (near) (5)
22 Square inch, say (8)
24 Muscle malady (4)
25 "Welcome" item at the door (3)
27 Struck (9)
28 Give a meal to (4)
30 ___-Mana-Mou, famous race horse (3)
31 Brothers' titles (4)
32 Destroy, as a pumpkin (5)
33 Spectrum start (3)

Down

2 Opposite of scarcity (8)
3 Single-named singer of "Smack That" (4)
4 Ancient capital of Macedonia (6)
5 Pres. on a 1970s dollar (3)
6 Noisy riotous fight (5)
7 Rabat robe (6)
9 Wolf, to Rocco (4)
13 Polish anew (5)
15 Listed in detail (8)
16 Idle sorts (9)
17 Inform in detail (7)
18 Track fixture (9)
21 Slangy head (4)
22 ___ Reader (alternative media digest) (4)
23 House of wax? (6)
26 Like a king (5)
29 "Guardians of the Galaxy" title characters, informally (3)

CROSSWORD 100

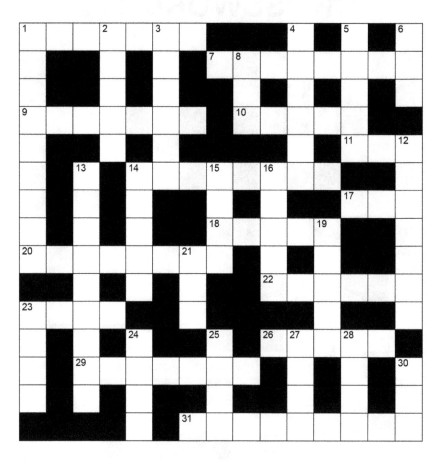

Across

1 Like the healthiest corned beef (7)
7 "The Canterbury Tales" character (8)
9 Paraphrase, perhaps (7)
10 Dude who knows how to create a buzz (5)
11 Calls between friends (3)
14 Places for germination (8)
17 Quick-trick card (3)
18 Computer game format (5)
20 Unstable particles (8)
22 Popular retirement city, informally (6)
23 Do ___ thing (4)
26 Pepé ___, amorous cartoon skunk (5)
29 Enthusiastic show of approval (7)
31 Balance also called lever scales (9)

Down

1 First Lady before Michelle Obama (9)
2 Cranes' bases? (5)
3 He declined the 1964 Literature Nobel (6)
4 Went all over (6)
5 "Footloose" Loggins (5)
6 Military award (3)
8 Sales pro (3)
12 Good and mad (7)
13 Fountain drink containing grape juice and vanilla ice cream (9)
14 Cold weather wear (5)
15 A.M.A. members (4)
16 Takes home, as salary (5)
19 Trounce (5)
21 Gp. with Bucks and Bobcats (3)
23 All at ___ (suddenly) (4)
24 Competition for a pennant (4)
25 Price paid (4)
27 Area of E.P.A. purview (4)
28 Fitzgerald known for her vocal jazz improvisation (4)
30 "Pore ___ Is Daid" ("Oklahoma!" song) (3)

ANSWER KEY

ANSWER 01

ANSWER 02

ANSWER 03

ANSWER 04

ANSWER 05

ANSWER 06

ANSWER 07

ANSWER 08

ANSWER 09

Across/filled letters:

COAL MINERS | SLIT
O | O | | T E | M
OWNERS | CHEER UP
L | O | E | E | T
J | S | I | A PEAK | K
EYE TESTS | E | A
R | O | I | PASSERS
KENNELS | M | N | T
I | H | A | EAR
AMICES | RAT SON | O
S | D | V | G | H | S
EVIL EYE | G | E | I
A | D | N | MAESTROS
I | R | A | A
TEST RIDES | SHU

ANSWER 10

INSTRUCTION CARD
H | O | R | A | E | P
REPULSED | M | P
E | X | E | GET MAD
P | E | P | H | I
SIDEWAY | ENDEARS
U | O | R | W | I | M
M | GASLESS | SNEAD
MOS | P | V | S | N
I | A | A | L | D
TELL ME | THEMED
L | A | O | A | L | A
VERANDA | D | AZUR
E | G | O | SATAN | G
ROOT ROT | O | OTTO

ANSWER 11

EMERSONS | MOANER
N | P | T | N
EARWAX | LOOSES | T
R | Y | A | A | N | U
GENIE | D | LIL | I | M
Y | A | DRILL | L | P | M
TRY | S | CIDERY
E | R | D | M | E | R
MEASURING | MUSTY
A | T | N | S | A | D
IRENE | SEALERS | S
L | I | C | A | E | H | L
SKIN | R | V | GLOSS
E | O | EGO | N | A
EXTRACTS | BERTH

ANSWER 12

SYSTEMS | RADIOS
T | A | L | H
ARSENATE | I | DIE
N | C | O | Y | B | C | F
D | O | O | REDIRECT
ORIBIS | N | N
T | P | C | ABUTS | A
A | I | H | T | E | N
MOON DANCE | RIDE
P | C | T | S | S | E
AEIOU | HIT THE HAY
L | S | E | D
OLE | CUL DE SACS
I | S | L | E
SNEAKERS | GILAS

ANSWER 13

R	O	U	N	D	T	R	I	P	S				S		
A						R			N	O	N	O	O		
S	P	A	M		L	A	T	I	N	A			O		
C		V		I		M		M		W					
A	D	A	M		S		E		E					G	
L		R		U	P	S	E	T		S	A	V	E	R	
		I		P		A		I						A	
A	C	C	T		S	L	A	M	S		G			N	
N		E		E		L		E	M	U		N		D	
O			T	A	C	O		I		S	A	T	S		
D		T	R		W	H	O	L	E		W		L		
I		O	R	L	Y		U		E		A	N	N	A	
Z		M	O		R		R	Y	L					M	
E		E		B	A	D	T	A	S	T	E				
S	H	I	R	E								C	H	A	R

ANSWER 14

N	I	A	C	I	N			S	T	E	E	P	S	
A		L		N		D				T			I	
S	W	E	E	T	L	O	V	E		U		Z		
A			E		O			A	L	I	C	E		
L	E	N	I	N	G	R	A	D		R				
		D		D		D		E	L	O	P	E		
P	R	E	S	T	I	G	E		L		A			
L		S		E		D	E	E	P	S	I	X		
T	A	T	T	O	O		S		S		E			
I								A	S	P	S			
D	E	D	A	D	A	D	A					K		
T		U	D	E	B		A	L	F	I	E			
Y		L	A	R	N		G		I	E				
C		E	M	P	T	Y	N	E	S	T		C	O	T
O	U	R		T			R		S			T		

ANSWER 15

L	A	P	D	A	N	C	E	S		M	A	C	K	S	
I		E		O		A		R					I		
V		M		O		L	A	D	A	D	O	G		H	
E	L	M	I	R	A		A	R					T		
L		L		L		D		A					S		
Y	E	S	L	E	T	S		B	K	I	T	E		
	X		E		O			A		M	A	E			
O	I	L		A	R	R	A	Y		O		E		
	L	C		S			S								
S	E	R	A	P	H	S		T		S				
L		M		I			U	N	C	L	A	D		
E	Y	E	O	N		G	E	S	T			E		
E		D						E	A	R	N	C		
P	R	E	M	E	D	S		R		G	P	A		
S		N				S	E	C	T			F		

ANSWER 16

S	I	A	M	E	S	E	C	A	T			W		S
	D							R	E	T	A	R	S	
A	L	M	A		A	R	E	P	A		L		E	
	E		M		E			I		Y	E	S		
R	U	B	E	N	S			T		S		B		
O			O			I	R	I	S		L	A	M	A
G	O	P			D	K		E			E	D		
M			S	O	U	P	E	D		O		L		
E			E		A		A	J	A	X		O		
F	R	O	N	T	A	L		S			B	E	S	
R		C		I			G		D	U		E		
U	T	E	S		N	I		A	M	O	U	R		
I		L				P	A	R	S	O	N			
T	W	O		V						T	R	A	C	Y
Y		T	E	N	D	E	R	I	Z	E				

ANSWER 17

ANSWER 18

ANSWER 19

ANSWER 20

ANSWER 21

Grid 21:
- ALIENTO, R, D, PGA
- S, M, GENIES, C
- POLISCI, L, R, IMA
- E, S, O, NOMESS
- NAUSEATE, A, K, N
- D, I, R, WARPAGE
- D, O, S, E
- RENDERING, E, S
- E, E, T, I, SOUL
- SCALENE, R, R, O
- S, I, MEACULPA
- S, MTS, U, S, A, N
- T, E, TOSSTO, N, E
- AILES, P, L, D
- Y, D, ASTA, ECOLI

ANSWER 22

Grid 22:
- HASAYEN, EXPORT
- I, L, E, I, K
- GRISELDA, ONTOUR
- S, P, I, E, A
- T, ROSSETTI
- PARISH, A, A, R
- O, N, E, L, NOVAS
- T, SENNETT, D
- RIT, R, AZTECS
- H, ACOAT, D, O
- O, L, A, L
- I, LANTERNS, L
- SYNS, E, I, ETUDE
- T, E, SALAAM, G, D
- SNOWY, K, IRON

ANSWER 23

Grid 23:
- TROUBLE, RANKS
- H, P, R, G
- ISSUER, PRIOR
- N, T, A, S, E
- AMASSED, TETLEY
- I, N, T, ETTA, I, C
- RIDE, C, CONGER, O
- S, RELOCK, O
- N, E, A, H, O
- SOCIALS, I, C, O, S
- O, L, L, SUNBONNET
- A, ASIDE, E, E
- R, M, S, RANDS, M
- OUTSOLD, I, S
- NOR, S, ASPECT

ANSWER 24

Grid 24:
- ANTENNA, IWISH
- F, E, C, O, A
- TOILETTE, W, H, I
- E, N, U, CAREERS
- R, B, BEAU, R, D
- BABA, L, S, O, Y
- W, L, R, IMUS, DDE
- E, ATEAT, ITI, E
- TON, B, Y, L, ALPO
- CHOP, A, E, R
- RYE, N, H, NOTME
- O, NEGLIGEE, E
- LED, S, A, R, DAT
- E, U, SHILOH, A
- STOOGES, UPS

Row 1: A U T E U R · P I E C H A R T
Row 2: B · L U E · D · · · E
Row 3: S A Y N O M O R E · · P
Row 4: E · I · I · B O D E S
Row 5: N I N B R E D · A · A
Row 6: C O O · O H A R A · B
Row 7: E P D T B N S C
Row 8: S T O O G E S · L A · A
Row 9: · L N · F A I R Y · R
Row 10: · H I H A T · W I O T
Row 11: · T · S P A R E T I R E
Row 12: P I E R · I E Y A P
Row 13: S · C · B A N A N A · A N O A
Row 14: E O I E C G M
Row 15: L O S E S · S T E E P L E S

Row 1: D E R · F R E E · · · H
Row 2: E · I · A · · A R O M A
Row 3: S · N E W O R D E R · I
Row 4: · G N U · E U C H R E
Row 5: H A T H · P A R I S · I D
Row 6: I O H O E E O C
Row 7: H U N G A R I A N · L A
Row 8: A E M M R E A S K
Row 9: T E S L A · O · X Y C
Row 10: S · I S P · W A V E
Row 11: · A N N E M E A R A · S D
Row 12: I G O I A A
Row 13: S T A B S · S C R A M B L E R
Row 14: O T O I M L S
Row 15: D E S P I S E S · T E E N

ANSWER 29

ANSWER 30

ANSWER 31

ANSWER 32

ANSWER 33

ANSWER 34

ANSWER 35

ANSWER 36

ANSWER 37

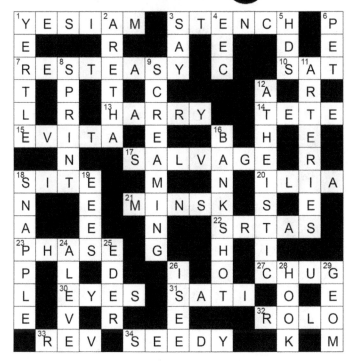

ANSWER 38

ANSWER 39

ANSWER 40

ANSWER 41

```
S T I C K   . B . N . C .
S . . O . P E R F O R A T E
E . . H . L . A . S . R . C
. S U A S I O N . H A R P O
. N . N . E . L . N . . U .
H A T . C U T S I T . K . M
. P . A . . T . P A R I S .
A P O S T R O P H E . . . C
. L . S . N . S N O W P E A
L E T T E R E D . E . . . D
. . R . . L . . . F . D
Q U E E N B E E S . N A N O
. M . O . . H . M . N
S P O K E N . G A B F E S T
. . . . . G . R . O
```

ANSWER 42

```
N O R M A N . A . C P A S
A . . . S . A G R A . D .
P L O P S . A . E . R A . F
O . . . E Z I N E . N O T T E
L Y R E S . D . S E . E A
I . H . . C A T E R S . . S
. . I . M . Y . . A L O T
. N E T C O S T S . B . I
I L E . S . N . E . A S L A N
M . . . I . T . P . A . G
P . M A N H O L E . L . T
A M Y . A . . E N C O R E
L . H A I K U . E . M . A
E . A . . . . A . E M F
S T A R L I G H T
```

ANSWER 43

```
I N T R U D E . M . N A S
R . E . . D O Z I N G . C .
A M A Z I N G . T . E A C H
N . S . R . E N D R U N . E
G . E . O . . E . O . P
A B S E N T E E . P A R T S
T . L . H . . A . . T
E N G I N E E R S . N
. I . T . A . T A K E
G . G O O S I N G . L . A
E . O . P . S . C A L M
A L S O . S N E E S . T . I
T . B . E . . T A K E . N
A . M E A G R E L Y . G
B . R . D
```

ANSWER 44

```
P R O M I S S O R Y N O T E S
R . R . . T . O . E . E
O D E L L . A L O U D . N . C
M . O . N . N . D . A
O . S O L I D I F Y . E . D
T . I . O . I . K O R E A
E . S V . F . R . A
R U P E E . F L E A . A G E E
S . A . B . N . E . B
. D I A N A R O S S . O
I K E . I . E . W . T A N
S . T A P S T E R . H . Y
T A U T . W . T . R I O
H . S . M A B E L S . N
E K E S . Y . D . M E G S
```

ANSWER 45

```
H E L D T H E F O R T
  O   O         O N
S U N G O D   L O S E Q
  G   K   M   M   M U
  C E O R   K   L O G I C
R O O N O T T R U E   R
R   N   F   I   B A S E L
  P   F I E S T A T   O
N O T A T E       N   B
  C   R     K   O S   S
  S A H L   M O O N S H O T
  U   I   E   P   L   E
M I S L A I D   C O O L E R
  M   I   R       E   P S
D A D     L E N D L
```

ANSWER 46

```
F A T T E N S   R E A G A N
I     E           T   I
R O O M   B   T   A   S
E     P   E Y E F U L L   J
D E L E T E   A   E   U
R   R   F A R S I   U S E D
I M E A S Y     E   S E E
L   J     R A I L C A R
L I E D   R   L   O   T
  C   A   A   A P P S   A
L I T T L E M E N   E R C A
O   I   T   O   T   N   T
D E N T E   S T E A M I R O N
Z   G   A   I   B   C   N
M A N E T S   E L E E
```

ANSWER 47

ANSWER 48

ANSWER 49

```
A M A Z I N G   A M A S S E S
G   L   V       A     I     T
N O I S E     T   Z   A L O E
E           O P E C   E     P
S C O R P I O N     A I N T
  A   E   M   G I L L   C
  S P E C I E S     L I E N S
  E   D   T       E       E
  M     A L R E A D Y     N
K E R M I T     L   I     A
  N   A   O L D E S T   P I T
  T A R   R     M     R   O
D     T     P   I N L A B O R
M U T I L A T E S       Y
X     N     S     E L S A S
```

ANSWER 50

```
A G A R I C         R A T S O
B   S   T   O   H         I
S S   S E N A T E   W E L D
O R E O       C   A   A   L
L   R   S T E V E D O R E   N
V   T   V       S   N       O
E T S   A M O   S     I R O N
        A F R I C A N       A
  F   A   N   G     G       M
F A U N   L O B O       A N E
  I   C   E     U   S   L   S
  T R I V I A   R A T I O
A     E   T   N   O   E B N
N     N A P O L E O N I   A
T E N T     N   Y   E   C D S
```

ANSWER 51

```
  G   N C I S   Y E L L O W Y
R E D O   C   W   X       W
  E   T O E L O O P       N
  S D   R     O L D E R
  E C O L I   L   U     R   O
      N   M A D O N N A S   L
  D E E   B   S   D   H   D
  E     L E A F     P I X Y
S E R A   A   A   R   P   E
  P   F   T R I M A   L
  S   F     R I N G   H   L
  I D A H O   N   I N U R E
  X   I   M O T O W N   L   R
R E A R   E   R   G R A M
  S   S U N R A
```

ANSWER 52

```
            S   O       K
S   P   U   M O O R E D   A
P L A I N   S   B   I     T
I   T   T A R O T   H   A D A M
N O R   A       H   M     R
E   I   M A P L E S   O F I T
  M O L E   I   O M A N     N
    T       C   O   D E A L
F D A   T   C H A R D S       O
  U   C U O M O       E   A Z O
M R T   R   L O W S   A       S
E     K E N O   I   E L E V E
S A D   R   D       E       S
  L     O Y E C O M O V A   T
S E R E       W       E
```

ANSWER 53

G	I	A	N	T	S			R		T	A	L	I	A		A
A			A			P	O		R			R		R
M	E	L	I	S	S	A		N	E	C	K	T	I	E
E		M		S		S				W			A
B		C	A	L	I	B	E	R		M	A	N	S
A		X		L	T			G		I
G	E	E		Y		T	A	I	W	A	N
	G		C			L		N		B		V
O	P	I	O	N	E	E	R	S		A		E
I		O	V		I		E	I	S	N	E	R
C	A	L	L	E	D	I	N		E		T
E		A	N		N		G	I	S	T		I
M	A	R	I			R		T	O		C
E		I		E	L	O	P	E		O	A
N	S	H	A	L	L		T		M	A	N	L

ANSWER 54

A	F	A	R	E	W	E	L	L	T	O	A	R	M	S
	I		I			Y	O		T			I
	G		T				R	E	N	D	E	R	E	D
C	A	M	E	L	L	I	A		A			E
	R		A	C		S	O	A	M	I		R
O	R	D	I	N	A	L		L		D		E
J	E		D		N		A	L	I	B	A	B	A
E	D				T		B		H		L
T	I	M	E	R	S		E		I	O
S	E	E			A	M	N	E	S	I	A	C
	S	A	R	D	I	S		E		N
H		T	E		S		E	L	D	E	S	T
I	T	S	L	A	T	E		E		I		E
P		L		S	E	A	R		N		R
S	S	I	T	E	S			M	E	D	I	C

ANSWER 55

N	I	C	E	G	U	Y	S		R		M		A
	N		R			O	N	E	R	O	O	M
R	E	C	O	R	D	E	R		S		P		A
	R			T	H	E	W	E	B
T	O	M	B	O	L	A		A		D		N
L		A		E		M	T	G	S		R
L	Y	R	I	C		A	T	E		S	A	L
I		O	K	K	E					O
E	A	B	E	A	M	T	O	O	W	S	W
I	D	R	G		M		C
N	M	U	S	S	E	L		C	A	R	D
S	A	P	E	L	L	E		A
O	P	S	I	M	E	R	I	P	S
N	S	N	Y	M	E	T		P
N	E	T	S		A	S	U	D	S	Y

ANSWER 56

P	O	P	L	A	R		T	S	H	R	E	D	S
R		O			A	V	E		A		T
O	P	E	R	A	T	O	R	E		G	A	T	O
O		E	F		O	S	H	A		O
F		T	O	W	S	E	R		M		D	P
R	U		O	M		I	V	I	E	S
E	O	R	D	E	R	F	O	R	M	E
A	N	T	L	O	T
D	E	F	E	N	D	S	U	R	N	S	A
U	E	I		I	G	P	S
A	G	O	H	A	N	G	O	N	T	O	P
E	S	D	F	N	L
I	N	D	E	X	E	R	T	A	S	T	I	E	R
I	C	M	E	A	U
M	E	L	S	U	T	N	E	P	A	I	R

ANSWER 57

ANSWER 58

ANSWER 59

ANSWER 60

ANSWER 61

ANSWER 62

ANSWER 63

ANSWER 64

ANSWER 65

ANSWER 66

ANSWER 67

ANSWER 68

ANSWER 69

ANSWER 70

ANSWER 71

ANSWER 72

ANSWER 73

SCREEN NAME — STAR — EXOD — MERLIN — LAWN CARE — BEAK — LOSE HOPE — TREET — MINXES — IRISED — OYE — SLOE — EEKS — DIME — REMIT — INSURES — PREP

ANSWER 74

AUGMENT — MAHATMA — SHIMMER — DETOUR — LATE GAME — TREE — ABDUCTION — SNOB — MATT — PLATTE — CIMINO — HITTITE — KOBE — SUSHI — SOUVENIRS

ANSWER 75

ANTHEMS — ARMY MEN — EASE UP — DOC — ENDS — CHASMS — IGNORE — DEEPENED — ELSE — DUNE — OLYMPIAN — HAZELS — EIGHT — SOA — TIERS — NOTEPADS — OMG — SISI

ANSWER 76

USED CARS — SIGHS — GAG WRITER — OSTE — EVENS — DIRTY TRIX — SLOT — SOPORS — GAITS — MEETS UP — TROTS — ORC — SPELT — INHALE — ANAP — TIN

ANSWER 77

ANSWER 78

ANSWER 79

ANSWER 80

ANSWER 81

```
L E E R E D [ ] F [ ] L E N A
A [ ] E [ ] A I R I L Y [ ] [ ] M
W [ ] B [ ] D [ ] [ ] T K O [ ] K
N E W A G E [ ] L A S S I E [ ] K
D [ ] E [ ] S [ ] N [ ] S [ ]
A L M A N A C [ ] C [ ] N O T I
R [ ] O [ ] E [ ] O N E U E [ ] O
T [ ] P [ ] R [ ] T S P E E D E R
S P I N A L [ ] M [ ] V [ ] E
[ ] E [ ] T [ ] R M O S E Y
A R E E N T E R [ ] T
I [ ] L [ ] E [ ] A P E S S
N [ ] B [ ] V A T I C A N A
T O R O [ ] T [ ] R [ ] S
I [ ] W R I S T S T I N T S
```

ANSWER 82

```
R S H A C K [ ] S I L E N T A A
E [ ] G [ ] O T [ ] M [ ] L
V [ ] L E N D E R [ ] B [ ] A
E A D I E [ ] A [ ] E [ ] M A N O R
R [ ] E [ ] A [ ] J P G [ ] L [ ] M
S W A R M E D [ ] L [ ] A M A T I
E [ ] D [ ] L [ ] E [ ] S
B A J A [ ] A [ ] S A D E T
S E E [ ] B [ ] R O E [ ] N
A E R O [ ] S [ ] A [ ] C
S S T [ ] R [ ] E [ ] N O V E L
E [ ] S T R A I N [ ] C [ ] A
E [ ] E [ ] T [ ] A E N A T E
E [ ] E [ ] E E L S [ ] E [ ] A
S C E N T [ ] S [ ] B A N G S
```

ANSWER 83

```
D E M O C R A T [ ] L G E S
I [ ] E [ ] O R S O [ ] C H E
A L L O W [ ] T R O L L
N [ ] B [ ] E S [ ] D E N E B B
T I T M O U S E [ ] C A E
H [ ] O Y [ ] G O G O R A
U [ ] G H [ ] I L I U M E
S A B A T E S [ ] N O E
E T [ ] T W I S T S D
K O D [ ] A [ ] D H
D L [ ] R E R E A D S
S H E L L S [ ] A R L
A [ ] E T [ ] E L M E R O
A G E D [ ] A [ ] L M S
A S C A R E D Y C A S H
```

ANSWER 84

```
O B S T I N A T E [ ] P A L L
[ ] D S [ ] E
P I M I E N T O [ ] N A O M I
I [ ] I A R [ ] A L A
P K [ ] W O R L D C L A S S
E L A T E [ ] I D U C
D [ ] T I T I I [ ] R E O
M T O S S A A T I M E T
R T M C A [ ] I S L
A A W E A T H E R N
I T R E B A T S
K N E E S S T L W
E U G R A V E N A
R E D D E R A Y N
S R C H E E R S
```

ANSWER 85

```
L A R I A T S       A     T
  D O   L     O H G R O W U P
  O     I     B     A   D   U
P R E L A T E S     B     D R
  E     R     M   P A I S E
S E T S       O     Y     U
T       A C C E N T S     E
E       L O A     A D D S
T W I R L I N G     N     E
S   S I     L     T H E R E M
    O V E R D R I V E     D M
R A T S   R   E     I     O N
E   O   S I G N S O N     N
E   P     E   E     S     E
F L E E T E R   E A R T H L Y
```

ANSWER 86

```
L A T T I C E S     L     N S F
  L   A       A R O A R       E
  D   P       G C   A Y E S   T
  O V E R R E A C H   M       T
  U   E         S L A N G
I S I T T I M E   R   F   A   U
R     R       F   E   G A T U N
A   D I E H A R D S   T   Y   S
N O N   E   X   E   B     Y   E
I   I   V       R   L
G   E C L A I R   R I L   C A E N
  T H O R   O   C R I L
  R   O   C   O N E T O   G
M O T H   S   S   F   V   E
  T     R I V E T S   E X E S
```

ANSWER 87

ANSWER 88

ANSWER 89

ANSWER 90

ANSWER 91

ANSWER 92

ANSWER 93

U	N	I	T	A	S		M	A	S	Q	U	E	S
N		M		R				L					H
P		B	Y	T	H	E	W	A	Y		I	L	A	Y
U		I			D		D	D			N		M
B		B		T		M		D	D		G		I	B
L		I	R	A	L	E	V	I	N				L
I		N		L		E	N			J	O	N	E	S
S		G	A	L	A	S							I
H			E		E	Y	E	S	O	R	E	S
E	L	L	I	S			Y		L		L
D		A		T	S	P	E	E	D	O	S
W		M		F		S		I		E	E	R
O	D	E	T	T	A		N	O	S	E	I	N	A
R		A		N			R		V		U
K	E	R	R		S	E	E	N	O	E	V	I	L

ANSWER 94

E	G	O	T	I	S	T	S			T
M	G		M		P	R	O	Z	A	C
P	R	O	N		A	E		K		T	O
R	D		R	A	N	A	F	T	E	R	R
E		R		T	T		S		E
S	T	R	U	D	E	L		A	L	T	A	I	R
S		N	S		N	E		R	O
A	S	H	E	L		G	L	A	N	D	S
A	A		I	E		U
N	O	R	T	H	P	O	L	E	G
I	E	P	R		D	W	E	E	B
R	N	S	H	D	C	S	N	A
A	T	O	A	H	T	E	S	T	C
N	I	S	E	I	L	O
I	N	D	U	E	I	D	S	T	I	R	S

ANSWER 95

E	B	R	O		M	T	F	U	J	I		H	I	T
D			B			O				U			I
I		S	H	A	S	T	A		H	A	N	D
T	M	I	R		H	E	S	S	O		E
	T		T		O	T	P	P
C	S	P	A	N	Y	S	H	O	G	U	N
T	O	B	E	M	T		N	C
E	E	N		A		M	A	P	C
R		T	M	A	T	T	O	D	I	E
M	B	A	S	S	E	V	E	N	T	N
M	X	G	A	O	I
N	O	L	I	E	R	A	D	I	I	C	N
V	C	O	M	O	P	E	S	O
I	H	A	T	E	T	O	W	L	D
E	B	D	S	H	A	P	E	L	Y

ANSWER 96

P	E	S	E	T	A		T	U	S	S	L	E	S
O		L	E		A		W	E	O
I	N	A	S	T	A	T	E	E	M	I	R	I
T	M	H		E	S	R
I		S	T	E	E	L	E	T	O	U	P	E	E
E		L	E	R	E
R	O	O	T	O	U	T	O	D	E	E	S
C	P	E	A	R	L	E	H
S	E	W	H	I	E	M	B	A	Y
A	S	T	R	I	K	E	U	P
N	R	S	N	E	S
D	S	L	O	E	L	T	O	N	J	O	H	N
A	A	N	N	E	V	I
S	L	E	L
H	E	S	I	T	A	T	E	R	U	B	B	L	E

ANSWER 97

ANSWER 98

ANSWER 99

ANSWER 100

THANK YOU

9 781951 791650